To
Kath,
Merry Christmas (2018)
sis - lots of love
Christine & Chris.
+
+

Our Street

# Our Street
## Growin' up in the 1950s

Written by Brian Carline

Illustrated by David Summerville

*For my mum and dad*

Previous page: Terraced houses 1958 copyright Philip Capper/Wikimedia Commons

First published in 2017
by Palatine Books,
Carnegie House,
Chatsworth Road
Lancaster  LA1 4SL
www.palatinebooks.com

British Library Cataloguing-in-Publication data
A catalogue record for this book is available from the British Library

ISBN 13: 978-1-910837-12-2

Designed and typeset by Carnegie Book Production
www.carnegiepublishing.co.uk

Printed and bound by Ashford Colour Press

# Contents

Introduction 1

The Fusilier's Arms 7

The Nuttall Family 19

The McGowan Family 29

The Barlow Family 37

The Birdsall Family 47

Mr Fairclough 59

The Goodbody Family 69

The Hennessey Family 77

The Acheson Family 87

The Turnbull Family 97

Mrs Anderton 105

Saint Sebastian's Church 115

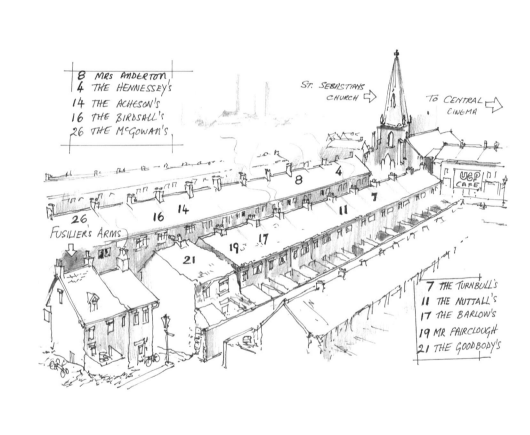

8 MRS ANDERTON
4 THE HENNESSEY'S
14 THE ACHESON'S
16 THE BIRDSALL'S
26 THE McGOWAN'S

ST. SEBASTIANS CHURCH ⇨

TO CENTRAL CINEMA ⇨

UCP CAFE

8

4

7

16   14

26

11

FUSILIERS ARMS

17

21

19

7 THE TURNBULL'S
11 THE NUTTALL'S
17 THE BARLOW'S
19 MR FAIRCLOUGH
21 THE GOODBODY'S

# Introduction

COPENHAGEN STREET WAS NO DIFFERENT from any street in any large industrial town or city in the 1950s. Many streets, similar to this one, were named after famous battles in our history. Copenhagen Street was, therefore, flanked by Trafalgar and Nile Streets. In other parts of the city, Crimea Terrace, Sebastopol Flats and Inkerman Place were again on the map as a testimony to our former military achievements. Copenhagen Street, like the rest, was cobbled, its pavements scarred, and some had cast iron lamp-posts festooned with an old bicycle tyre or a length of old lorry rope, swinging in the breeze.

Houses were identical, two up, two down terraced properties, and back to back. Most women living in these abodes religiously donkey-stoned their front doorsteps and window sills. It showed a pride in their property. Errant families lived in houses with cracked or boarded-up windows, and their steps were never washed and cleaned. Some streets were blessed with a pub or a corner shop, whereas others boasted a chippy or a church.

Most properties were rented and the rent man's purposeful and unforgiving knock on a Monday morning would remind residents of their budgets for the rest of the week. Rent money was usually gathered from a tin or vase on the mantelpiece and woe betide any family whose mums had too many port and lemons, or dads who had quaffed an excess of mild, the Saturday night before. Rent had to be paid or you were out on the streets. An equerry to the Queen visited

1

the city prior to the Queen's visit in 1954. He noticed tables and chairs on the pavements of streets in the poor areas of the city.

'Is that what we call dining *al fresco*?' he inquired.

'Err … no, sir,' replied Mister Mayor. 'Round here, we call that eviction!'

*Our Street* depicts a typical street in any large industrial town or city in the North of England. Its residents were often those with large families, whose kids had to top and tail at bedtime. They shared second-hand clothing or hand-me-downs. It was an age of 'make-do and mend'. Darning, sewing and recycling were all in a mother's repertoire.

Many parents would worry where the next meal was coming from, and so visit the pawnbroker, exchanging bedding or a wedding ring for a few bob to tide them over 'til the end of the week, at twenty percent interest. Grans and mums were the family's triage nurses, having been brought up in times prior to the inception of the National Health Service in 1948. Ailments and injuries were self-treated, hence terrifying remedies such as the use of bread poultices for boils, and a doorknob and strong cotton for tooth ache featured in their prescriptive handbook.

Some families in the street could just make ends meet and were tempted by the appeal of hire purchase, and paying the tallyman 'on the drip'. Copenhagen Street was home to working class people. Despite hard times, the majority of these people maintained a sense of dignity and possessed an irrepressible sense of humour. A popular pub comedian would start his act by asking the noisy audience, 'How's yer debt?' Men would walk to work in overalls and caps. Some would ride their bicycles to the pit, the mill or Trafford Park. Women would juggle countless jobs to feed the family to keep them together. In the street there was a sense of community, mutual support and trust. Nobody stole from their neighbours, and anyway, there was simply nothing worth stealing.

A front door key was tied to a piece of string and left dangling inside the letter box. People would walk into each other's houses for a natter and listen to gossip they had missed down at the wash house. Families would help out other families. This assistance came in the form of cups of sugar or an old pair of kid's shoes. An ageing grandma in the local pub would be seen pulling out a ten bob note, incubating from inside her bra, and saying to her daughter, 'No, I'll get this round in, love. You've got four children.'

All houses looked the same. Everyone had a front room or parlour. This was only used for when 'company' arrived or when some family member had died and was 'laid out' in there. This continued to make it a no-go area for the children. The living room was where the family ate and relaxed. A wooden table with an oil cloth was where you ate meals and mum would cut up the ingredients of tater hash. This room had a cast iron fire grate next to the oven which was freshly 'blacked up' each time the fire went out. Due to financial hardship many houses retained this Victorian style, whilst others would try to move with the times and try bright wallpaper and use spin dryers. Now that was viewed as progress and ultra-modern living.

The aspiring bourgeoisie of today boast about having a wet room in their house. In Copenhagen Street, like all other streets, in the forties and fifties most houses had plenty of them but this addition was referred to as rising damp. Windows often had ice on the inside panes during cold winter nights, and to keep warm in bed you always slept curled in the foetal position. Stone hot water bottles were like hugging a red hot meteorite. When they went cold you could hear them being pushed out of bed and landing with a deafening thump on the lino floor.

In some houses they retained a cold water tap positioned above a slop stone where pans were washed and water was drawn. Under the kitchen sink was a curtain behind which you would find a block of carbolic soap, a packet of Rinso and a bucket and scrubbing brush. The scullery had a mangle, designed to get rid of every drop of water from the washing, and every finger if you weren't too careful. A galvanised barrel acted as a wash tub, and was where the weekly wash was pummelled with the posser. After the washing had been done, this barrel was dried and used as a primitive play pen for crawling one-year-olds. Compassion was only shown when the baby banged its head on the cold, hard walls.

Warm water was available if you heated the copper. Baths were taken in the living room and the galvanised bath was placed on the rag rug in front of the fire. There was always a bathing protocol for each household. Usually the order of bathing was first the mother, then the kids, next the whippets and finally the husband.

Some streets had cellars housing the copper and involved a terrifying journey into the dark, dank bowels of the house. You held a lighted candle stuck on a saucer to light your way. Coal was tipped down the coal hole and was brought upstairs in a coal bucket. If the house had no cellar then the coal was dumped in a heap in the backyard. This area housed the outside toilet, a pleasure to use in the summer but gave you chilblains in the winter. Therefore, when you 'went', you didn't hang about. Many families would, once more, employ a lighted candle but this time place it by the cistern to prevent it from freezing. Lead pipes were sweated after they had burst but continued to give us toxic lead poisoning.

Some backyards had a dark, unwelcoming storage area behind the outside toilet. Many people referred to it as 'The Glory Hole'. Its nickname stemmed from the inhospitable trench dug outs scattered across Flanders fields in the 1914–18 war. The backyard door opened onto an entry or ginnel with a drainage channel running along its centre. Clothes-lines were hung across this passage and kids would duck under rows of sheets and shirts as they chased each other, playing games.

This was the 1950s and an age of post-war recovery. In those days, as youngsters we referred to having a left and a right leg. Today, as senior citizens, we now talk about having a good and a bad leg. For many they were hard but happy times. Some were one-parent families because dad sadly didn't make it back from the Burma campaign or Normandy. As kids we would play for hours on bomb sites and then come indoors for our tea. If we had a football that was a luxury, it was often a ball of old rags that was kicked about. If girls had access to their mum's cosmetics and old frocks, then they too created their own entertainment. Skipping ropes were either bits of old washing lines or a chaffed, thick lorry rope that would stink of diesel.

If you remember a childhood like this, then Copenhagen Street was your street. Its families and characters will be those you grew up with. So, please read on and recall those memories and take with you your sense of humour and imagination.

Brian Carline
March 2017

# The Fusilier's Arms

HORACE DEWHURST, LANDLORD AND LICENSEE of The Fusilier's Arms, Copenhagen Street, would boast that his grand hostelry purveyed cigarettes and cigars of the choicest brands and Threlfalls noted ales and stout, all in fine condition. Some of his customers would disagree, and one particular gentleman described his ale as having all legs and no body. Horace's quick temper silenced any further comparisons, and the poor critic was dispatched home minus two teeth.

Another selling point of this establishment was that it offered 'well-aired beds' for commercial gentlemen at the outstanding rate of six shillings and sixpence per night. Breakfast was taken in the back room but with an additional charge of threepence for use of the cruet.

The Fusilier's, as locals would call it, was a large, imposing red brick building at the bottom of our street. There was a cinder croft at the side. This flattened area resulted from the Luftwaffe's bombing of Tanner's engineering works instead of Trafford Park industrial complex, two miles away. The myopic bomb aimer must have wanted a quick return home.

In order to impress his fellow licensed victuallers, Horace would refer to this space as the pub's car park. However, none of Horace's punters possessed a car, and kids used it as a play area.

'Bugger off and mind me windows!' Horace would bawl as Manchester United were playing Luton Town on his car park.

'Go on! Clear off I tell ya. Ya've no right to be playin' here. Now, go on before I burst that ball. Bugger off!'

Threats and profanities of this nature may not have upset Sir Matt Busby but to us kids, Horace was a fearsome fellow and not to be messed with. We accepted his advice and played further up the street.

Horace was married to Lucrezia, an Italian lady who spoke with a hybrid patois. Her voice and pronunciation was a mix between Bari and Manchester speak. She would shout to an eager customer waiting to quench his thirst, 'Eh! Signore. Dona rush me, I only gotta one pair o' 'ands per favore!' Lucrezia had a ruddy complexion and her long, dark hair was always neatly tied back in a bun. She would be referred to as petite, and for most of the time she worked behind the bar, and was only visible from the chest up. However, despite her lack of height, she had chunky toned arms, ideal for drawing cask ales with the hand pump. Lucrezia could pull a decent pint with three long tugs. This was in contrast to the new barmaid, Eileen, whose pint with its deep frothy head always made you look like Father Christmas during a quick swig.

Horace had been in the Eighth Army when it was busy working its way up Italy from the Salerno landings in 1943. Part of the strategy to drive the Germans out of the country was for pressure to be put on the Wehrmacht on both east and west coasts of the country. Horace's platoon found itself under heavy fire, and had scattered throughout the countryside around Foggia. Horace took shelter in a barn on a farm owned by Lucrezia's father, who fortunately for Horace, had little sympathy for the Nazis. Lucrezia discovered Horace hiding in the barn, and took pity on this Mancunian vagabond. She hid him in the fields during daytime and would bring him back to the farm at night for food.

Horace's gratitude for Lucrezia's kindness towards him, and for putting herself and her family in danger, forced him to return to the farm at the end of the war, and to ask for her hand in marriage. She accepted, and soon the young farm girl from the beautiful Italian wheat yielding plains found herself behind a bar in a Salford pub, pulling pints. Two children, Bianca and Giovanni, completed their family unit.

The Fusilier's was thought to be a cut above the typical alehouses in the area. Horace was anxious that his pub should not be seen as a spit and sawdust premises. He refused to have a taproom that would attract the riff raff. Instead, the hoi polloi congregated at the neighbouring Craven Heifer. These premises had on many an occasion found it difficult to renew their licence because of its rowdy, drunken clientele, and the pub's sawdust floor had soaked up many pints of blood over the years. At The Fusilier's, on the other hand, there was the vault, a room that welcomed the general public, and whose sole purpose was to allow them to have a good, peaceful drink. Dirty work clothes were frowned upon, and any notorious 'ladies of the evening' who strayed from the docks area were quickly given their marching orders, and told to ply their trade at the Craven Heifer.

The vault welcomed its regulars. Men all dressed in similar clothes, all wearing a cloth cap. Collarless shirts were sometimes worn with an off-white muffler tied around the neck which draped over the top of their waistcoat. They wore patched demob suits and leaned against the bar, the elbows of their jackets soaked in beer.

Everyone seemed to smoke. Pipes, packed with such carcinogenic mixes as Dark Shag or Twist, emitted thick, sharp smoke fumes that attacked the back of your throat. Player's Weights, Woodbines, Senior Service, Navy Cut and Park Drive seemed popular behind most bars. Men would knock the tobacco in the cigarette on the packet before lighting it with a match. There were no cigarette lighters in the vault. Roll ups worked out cheaper than packet cigarettes, and their paper often took away the top layer of cells of your lips if you did not wet them with saliva first.

Pipe smokers would set fire to the tobacco and then proceed to defy pain by packing down the smouldering mass with blackened, fire retardant fingers. Accompanying the background noise of this room were alarming bouts of deep rumbling bronchial coughs that seemed to roll on forever. These episodes of lung clearing usually concluded with the words, 'Aye, that's better!'

It was the norm for men to queue outside pubs and wait for opening time. This was particularly noticeable on a Sunday when non church-goers (agnostics, pagans and orthodox 'can't be arsed') would wait outside for the midday door opening. The Fusilier's was just across the road from St Sebastian's Catholic Church. Its male congregation also worshiped at The Fusilier's, and were out of St Sebastian's even before the final Pax Vobiscum, soul cleansing and spiritual uplifting were followed, minutes later, by an alternative form of holistic therapy – a pint of Threlfalls.

Draught beer was either bitter or mild. Draught Bass was a leading competitor to most cask ales. Chester's mild was seen as an elixir of life and was quaffed with relish by many Lancastrians. Most men drank the house draught bitter because they would say the slops went into mild. Slops in bitter would spoil its clarity and was easily recognisable. In Horace's pub, slops went into everything, particularly if the customer already had five pints in his belly. At one shilling and threepence a pint, a man's weekly wage was vulnerable. Draught Guinness cost more. Bottles of Mackeson, milk stouts, pale ales and barley wines featured on shelves behind the bar. Optics dispensed whisky, rum and gin. Port and lemons, Babychams or Cherry Bs were poured for any ladies who should stray into this room. The absence of a snug in this pub made most ladies drink in the lounge.

The vault was a dark room even with the lights on. Nicotine- and tar-stained brown paintwork absorbed what little light there was. The two windows in this room were etched, frosted glass, both with the word VAULT, visible to the street. Running across the base of the bar counter was a brass foot-rail, scraped and scratched by clogs or work boots over the years. There were no bar stools. Everyone stood at the bar except the very old. There were wobbly wooden tables and benches for these wobbly customers to sit and recall past times.

The game of dominoes was permitted in the vault. This was a deadly serious exercise. Men with hands as tough as a Brillo pad would hold their six tiles close to their chest. They would put one hand of tiles face-down to sup their ale, and then pick up the dots again to continue the game. Should cheating be suspected it would have been punished the way card sharks were dealt with in the wild west, and given a one way visit to Boot Hill.

Unfortunately, the vault was often guilty of robbing families of their housekeeping. Many a pay packet on a Friday evening would be turned into more than a few gills by eleven o'clock the same night. The perpetrator would be scolded and humiliated by his wife on the Saturday morning. She had worked thriftily throughout the week to make ends meet only to be greeted with a reduced budget from her hung-over spouse. A visit to the pawnbroker would follow, where wedding rings, watches and even bedding were exchanged for a few bob to tide the family over until the end of the week.

The vault witnessed debate about football, horse racing, women, politics, working conditions and pay. Times were hard and a good chat with your mates over a couple of pints softened the daily grind. Humour increased in proportion with the ale consumed. Victor Aspinall, a welder at Cox and Danks, joked with Horace, 'Eh, Horry! That new barmaid you've taken on? Lovely bit o' stuff. Nice arse on her, an' all.'

'If you are referring to young Eileen, Vic, I don't know what you are talking about,' replied Horace.

'Get off, Horry. I saw yer last week. All over her you were like one o' them physiotherapists! Wasn't he lads?' The group of six agreed.

'She's new to the job. I was merely helpin' her find her feet,' was Horace's response to such an accusation.

'Find her feet, Horry? Find her arse more like!' Vic's quick wit brought endless laughter from the Vault regulars.

'And … I'll be grateful if there's none of that talk in front of my good wife, if you please. She may get the wrong idea,' Horace pleaded.

'Right idea, more like!' persisted Vic to his captive audience's delight.

The lounge bar was mainly used at weekends. It was a room where ladies were welcome. Husbands could bring their wives and courting couples could make eyes at each other and hold hands. Women could sit with other women and put the world to rights or gossip about the new family just moved in at number sixteen.

'Have you seen her? She had all her front teeth taken out and had a new fireplace put in!' Other condemnatory proclamations followed such as, 'She says that in her house, everything runs like clockwork,' to which a knowledgeable seventy-five-year-old granny would reply, 'Aye, clockwork, indeed! That's 'cos everything is on tick!'

A young man, an apprentice at Horsefall and Vickers engineering firm, and on a low budget, may find himself on a first date in the lounge of The Fusilier's. His partner is some voluptuous maiden, a packer at the Colgate Palmolive factory, and from her painted looks, she had taken ages to get ready. Being conscious of his lack of funds, yet still keen to woo and impress his new lady friend, he would shout to her from the bar, 'What are you havin' love? I hear the mild's good.'

Should she ask for a packet of crisps as well? Did she think that lad was made of money?

The room's bright, yet tired decor was matched with wooden

seats and stools, each with padded, plastic covers, clustered around easily wiped tables. Every table-top was complete with cigarette burns where punters couldn't be bothered to reach for an ashtray, and had left their cigarettes on the edge of the table. Several tables had round watermarks in their polish displaying years of use. One had five interconnecting circles. It resembled the logo for the Olympic games.

The linoleum floor was swept and scrubbed daily by Lucrezia with her mop and bucket. 'I no like de dirty feet on me pavimento!' she would say to Horace. He would lovingly nod to her in agreement, and accidentally drop ash from his Capstan Full Strength cigarette on her shiny pavimento.

Saturday nights in the lounge meant live music being supplied by Vince Crump and his Starlight Combo. This ageing ensemble, comprising Eric Poulter, Jimmy McEwan and Vince himself, would knock out hits of today and yesteryear. Jimmy was a drummer who bashed the skins as though there was to be no tomorrow. Eric, the pianist, would allow his fingers to run across the ivories like lightning. However, as lightning tends not to do, Eric's fingers never landed in the same place more than once. Vince rated himself as both crooner and trumpeter. Vince was said to be a blend of Matt Monroe and Eddie Calvert. The trouble was, he sang like Eddie Calvert and played the trumpet like Matt Monroe. Nevertheless, Saturday nights in the lounge bar of The Fusilier's, provided for many, the antidote to a week's hard labour at the nearby cotton mills, docks, collieries and Trafford Park.

Vince would frequently step down from the microphone and allow members of the audience to give their own vocal renditions of popular songs. It was a kind of 1950s karaoke. Songs such as 'You are my heart's desire,' would be interpreted by some inebriated customer as 'Hew … har my heart's deezire, hand where hew har … hi long to beeeee.' Such romantic sentiment was delivered to the Joseph Locke fans in the audience through a tinny microphone at an unbelievably high volume.

Diarmuid Phelan, an Irish patriot, ironically living in rooms off Britannia Street, would slay the punters with 'Danny Boy'. After his powerful performance, he would ask the audience for requests. Vera Weaver, a quick-witted market trader, would answer his enquiry with, 'Can ya sing far away, love?'

The stage struck, ingenuous Hibernian was seemingly immune

to criticism, and would then reply, 'I'm sorry darlin', I don't know the words to dat one.'

Leonard Blythe from Windsor Terrace put in a wonderful performance of the Bing Crosby number 'Don't Fence Me In'. This proved tragic irony, for, one month later, Leonard was given two years in Strangeways prison for burglary.

Always around closing time, some veteran of the Great War would stand up and sing 'Roses of Picardy'. Such an emotional tear jerker would receive tumultuous applause when he finished the final refrain, 'But there's one rose that dies not in Picardy, 'tis the rose that I keep in my heart.' The result – not a dry eye in the house. It must be remembered that every family, in every street, lost someone in the 1914–1918 campaign.

Saturday evenings saw Dick Prescott, the pot man, double as a waiter. Dick suffered from congestive heart failure and had defied death several times. Horace had taken pity on this seventy-year-old trainee corpse and given him the job of collecting empty glasses from tables on the busy Saturday nights. Dick's perks of the job allowed him to finish the dregs from glasses he collected. It didn't seem to matter to Dick if a mouthful of cream stout was followed with a lifeless snowball. 'It all goes down t'same 'ole!' was his rationale.

Dick would slowly meander between tables, often stopping to catch his breath. Dick's pace was that of a moribund slug. However, he was particularly skilled in using his arthritic fingers to hold five glasses in each hand then journey back to the bar to deposit these empties. Things would go well unless Dick suffered one of his 'nasty turns' as he called them. These sudden bouts of oxygen deficiency would be heralded by the sound of ten pint pots, smashing on the floor as Dick tried to unbutton his collar, to ease his desperate state.

As a waiter, he always remembered your order, and his importance and role with this thirsty clientele was underlined by him wearing a white cotton jacket and carrying a tray. Some granny would shout to him, 'Two pints o' mild, a barley wine and a Macky, love.' She would then put her hand inside her bra, bring out a ten bob note. The warm, incubated note would then be squeezed into Dick's beer-soaked hands. In practical terms, it would have been easier and quicker for them to have gone to the bar, bearing in mind Dick's slow pace.

The unique selling point of The Fusilier's Arms was an upstairs concert room. It was a fair-sized area with a small podium at the back on which artistes could perform. Its bar dispensed all of the house ales and spirits. Once more, there were tables and chairs set out around the room, to seat an audience. The furniture from the lounge that was deemed to be on its last legs was moved up into the concert room. To give this space a special, distinctive atmosphere, Horace referred to it as the Manhattan Suite. It was as close to class, prestige and luxury as the Seaman's Mission off Cross Lane. There were several photographs of celebrities hanging from the walls. Frank Sinatra was next to Lena Horne. Bing Crosby shared a space with Lucrezia's favourite vocalist, Mario Lanza. Should this American tenor come through on their Bush wireless, Lucrezia would shout to Horace, 'Ooooh Horry … turn him up cara mio. Una bella voce! Bellissimo.' Horace would smile and duly oblige.

An orange-coloured poster, starting to peel from the wall, boasted in large black letters 'COMING SOON! THE DALLAS BOYS'. This message had hung on that same wall for the past four years and still there was no sign of them. Horace would argue that contractual problems were responsible for their lack of showing.

'Are they coming or not?' argued Sydney Randle, a fitter at the East Lancs Paper Mill.

'I've told ya, they're comin',' replied an irate Horace, angrily pointing his finger at the gentleman.

'Aye … They're comin'. So's ruddy Christmas! They'll be 'The Dallas Old Gets' by the time they come 'ere,' was Sydney's reply. These words were in sharp contrast to the advice Horace then gave him, which was something to do with urination and going on a journey.

The Manhattan Suite was used on Sunday lunchtimes. Horace would refer to these sessions as a 'come as you please'. They were occasions where the locals could display their talents to an intoxicated audience that were about as welcoming as The Glasgow Empire. Artiste's names were put up in chalk, and compere Dave 'Lucky' Partridge hosted the show. Dave was an electrician by day and not a very good one at that. My granddad would say, 'Never trust an electrician with no eyebrows!' Indeed, Dave had no eyebrows and Dave's nickname 'Lucky' clearly highlighted the number of close brushes with death he had experienced doing his electrical jobs. Horace insisted Dave wore a tuxedo and bow tie. He had fancied himself as a magician in his earlier years and this same tuxedo bore remnants of canary and pigeon excrement down one leg where his concealed birds had been squeezed into the jacket lining.

Mavis Butterworth was a frequent participant at the Manhattan Room's Sunday extravaganza. Mavis was a ledger clerk at the council offices and was an extremely talented whistler. She was as good as Ronnie Ronalde, and her version of 'Birdsong at Eventide' was considered to be outstanding by the Manhattan Room occupants. She would stand centre stage and contort her lips whilst at the same time exhaling and putting her hands around her mouth. At times, her top set of dentures would resonate with notes emanating from her pursed lips. These NHS prostheses moved up and down with such frequency she looked as though she was shivering with cold. However, her efforts frequently won her first prize, usually a bottle of Drambuie and a packet of 20 Park Drive.

Less talented participants would continue with their act, despite calls of 'Gerroff', 'Rubbish' and 'Turn it in!' On occasions 'Lucky' Dave would jump onto the podium and draw to a close their painful efforts. One such performance was delivered by Tommy O'Rourke from Trevelyan Street, who once worked nights as a bakery technician. Tommy was recently fired for telling the public he used his dentures to crimp the pastry and even worse, what he used to put the holes in the doughnuts. He rated himself as a contortionist and insisted he be called by his stage name Ben Dover – an appalling *nom de plume*, I agree, and so was his act. Tommy and body bending were about as mutualistic as rabies and dogs. His act often terminated with some distal part of his anatomy in the wrong place and him being helped from the stage.

One Sunday lunchtime, Horace decided to book a professional act and support these aspiring artistes. The subtle motivation for him doing so was that the longer his audience was entertained, the more they would sup. His name was Desmond Croker – Memory Man Extraordinaire. His agent charged Horace twenty five shillings for a forty minute spot but unfortunately Des, preoccupied with many things on his mind, forgot to turn up. This was cerebral talent that would never get him an Equity card.

The management of The Fusilier's was shared equally by Horace and Lucrezia. Horace would attend to the draymen, change barrels, clean the pipes, liaise with the brewery and serve the punters. He was also in charge of the pub's off licence which was a tiny room accessed from the street. It was connected to the bar area by a frosted glass window that could be raised to serve the public. Young kids would run an errand for their mum or gran to purchase five Woodbines and a gill of ale.

Horace was good with Joe Public, being a good listener with a quick sense of humour. He was also someone you didn't cross, and such skills gave the pub a good local reputation. He would not be offended by truculent pensioners like Renee Birdsall, whose order was given to him at high volume and went something like, 'I want two milk stouts, Horace in clean glasses, if you please!' However, if any of his clientele were clearly the worse for wear, he would give them abrupt, indisputable instructions to go home. People said of Horace, 'If Horace refuses to serve you, then go home before he adjusts your dental records.'

Lucrezia also served behind the bar and was extra careful with the over-zealous cash till that would open its drawer like a bullet from a gun. Whereas Horace would arrest its surge with his corpulent belly, Lucrezia being a petite lady would stand back from it to save fracturing her jaw.

She looked after any residential bookings and would escort the commercial travellers to their room and announce 'Dee toilet and baffroom eese along dee corridor and mekka sure you aim properly. Breffass eese a seven tirty in dee back room, per favore.' Lucrezia also supervised the cleaner, Mrs Delaney. This woman could talk, and would frequently clash with Lucrezia over her lack of progress during the morning cleaning sessions.

'I no pay you for talkin'. Deee gents' toilet smells like a police horse has justa used eet. Getta de move on pigro vecchio vacca!'

These last three words posed problems for her English, but not for her Italian.

Horace rarely showed his emotions. The closest he came to tears was when their young son, Giovanni, contracted rheumatic fever and was feared lost to this unforgiving disease. Whenever Lucrezia was upset he would console her and give her a cuddle. They always kissed each other goodnight and she would make him his favourite cow-heel pie with gravy as viscous as crude oil. Horace knew she was homesick and that she secretly longed for the landscape of her native southern Italy. He never forgot the fact that she and her family had risked their lives to save this Manchester lad. All he had wanted was to give her a better life and to take care of her. Proceeds from the profits of the Sunday 'come as you please' would be put into a special account in Horace's name.

In 1965, an age of rebirth began in towns and cities across the country. Tired streets, with their shabby, war torn buildings, were earmarked for demolition. It was customary at the time to flatten whole streets but to leave the pubs and alehouses still standing for as long as possible. Residents were being rehoused in different areas of the city. Some had to move to far away from their neighbourhoods. Other casualties of this slum clearance moved to flats. Many waited for places in the new high rise towers, prescribed for the city's regeneration. Lucrezia became anxious about their future. It was at this time, and unknown to Lucrezia, that Horace revealed that he had saved enough money to take his beloved Lucrezia back to live in the wheat-growing plains of Tavoliere, around the principal city of Foggia, Italy. He never forgot he owed her his life. After twenty-two years of marriage and a hard life, running a city pub, it was now time for them to start a new life, and one that would allow their love story to continue. The couple moved to Italy in 1966 and continued to have many happy years together.

# The Nuttall Family
# at Number 11

'Yᴏᴜ'ʟʟ ʜᴀᴠᴇ ᴛᴏ ᴍᴏᴠᴇ them boxes of toilet rolls, Lenny. I'm fed up with it. I can't get the lavvy door closed. I'm sat there showin' me all to everyone!'

This ear-splitting request was issued by Nora Nuttall, beloved spouse of Lenny, a market trader who was a regular fixture at The Flat Iron Market at the top of Cross Lane. Lenny had a pitch there every Thursday, Friday and Saturday. To complete his working week he would travel as far as Bolton where he also held a busy licenced pitch.

'I'll shift 'em today my flower,' Lenny quickly replied. 'Anything for you my sweetness!' Lenny's interpersonal skills had been sharpened by years of dealing with the public. He also knew that his beloved Nora always responded well to these terms of endearment.

'Nothing is too much for you, my little cherub,' came yet another effusive compliment.

'Never mind all that rubbish. Yer not on yer stall now, butterin' up yer lady customers. Just get them boxes shifted. I nearly broke me neck, trippin' over 'em yesterday!'

'They're as good as gone, my sweet.' Lenny had now defused the conflict, in his inimitable way, and Nora was temporarily appeased.

The backyard of the Nuttalls' was always covered in blue tarpaulins. These sheets protected boxes of various domestic items, from pots and pans to small ornaments. Indeed, one of Lenny's regulars once said, 'You can get anything on Lenny's stall, from a washboard to a dinner set.'

Another lady would say of Lenny, 'I asked him for some of that perfume. Ya know, that French stuff, Channel Number 5. He got me some but the spelling on the box was wrong. They only put one N, not two. But it smelt alright, almost like the real thing!'

Lenny had a prime pitch at both markets. As soon as you entered the bazaar, there he was in a dominant position, right in front of you. Lenny stood on old crates, giving him an elevated view of his customers. The front of his stall was packed with colourful items and behind him sat the more expensive and glitzy articles. In the winter days, lights would pick out the shiny chrome of his cookware and the sea of reds and blues of his towels. His stall had the appearance of a grotto or Ali Baba's cave. Tilley lamps provided some form of heat for Len as he knocked out his wares on cold February days. The stall's brightness picked up the trail of water vapour from his mouth as he enunciated every chosen word for his customers. The set up was designed to have impact on the visiting public. It would draw punters to his stall like cheese on a mousetrap.

He was affectionately known throughout the city as 'Looney Len' because of his ability to convince his customers that he was giving away his merchandise. He had the patter of Max Miller and the ability to convince you that it was Saturday even if it was a Thursday. Lenny's two teenage sons also admitted, 'Dad could sell a packet of French letters to the Pope.'

Lenny had a simple philosophy about market trading in that he knew everyone wants something for nothing. His subtle banter with the public gathered around his stall would convince them that, indeed, they were getting products at rock bottom prices. Draw them in and hypnotise them with his outrageous patter then hit them with the bargain of the century. The hands would shoot up like toadstools in a woodland glade, and he'd take their money. Lenny would say, 'Nothing attracts a crowd better than a crowd.' He could then hold this spellbound group as they eagerly anticipated yet another bargain. 'Sweetners' as Lenny called them, would help maintain the population around him. The motivation for the crowd to remain was due to Lenny throwing out to his audience a bag of tea towels or a small toy. These freebies often saw people scrap for them like lions around a carcass. His understanding of the herd or crowd instinct made him save the best until last. By this time he had established a feeding frenzy, and this psychology caused his eager punters to pay more than they wanted, and still leave the market feeling they had secured a real bargain.

Humour was an integral part of Lenny's set. If you make them laugh they stay at your stall longer. This was an important rule for any marketeer. Years of trading had honed his presentation. He was famous for his ad libs, and hecklers had no chance at all. Lenny always had the final word. He didn't need a microphone; his oratory would easily cut through the morning air. To him, a day's trading was like performing in repertory. As Lenny advanced in years though, he became weary by the time the stall had closed and put to bed until the next day. He hoped his two sons would take over the business in a few years' time. Heaven knows, they had received excellent tutelage.

Lenny loved the market's atmosphere. There was noise everywhere. Cries from the fruit and vegetable stalls were often indecipherable.

'Pound o' nanas, luv, a bob ta you! Navels, git yer lovely navels, six for a tanner!' If you purchased oranges you would ask for the pink wrapping paper to be left on. As a male senior citizen with obvious problems once proclaimed, 'It makes smashin' toilet paper. It's dead soft on yer bum!'

In the distant rows, echoes of other traders rang through the air. There was vibrancy, which nurtured an atmosphere of excitement and opportunity.

One veg stall was home to a quick-witted purveyor, Sammy Thwaites, who, when asked if he'd put manure on the rhubarb he sold, replied 'Manure on me rhubarb? Not me darlin', I prefer custard. Don't you?' Sammy would talk to his passing clients and simultaneously turn the black patches on the bananas away from their view. The most risqué he would ever be was to shout to a young lady in curlers and headscarf, who had bought a bag of cherries from him: 'Here, hold on to your cherry love for as long as you can. That's a bit of fatherly advice … No, honest, there's pickpockets around today, darlin'!' The girl's cheeks would flush with embarrassment, and she would bow her head and smile as she moved on.

Lester Boothroyd sold meat and meat products. From a distance, this gentleman looked like Humpty Dumpty. His ovoid morphology was complemented with bright rosy cheeks and arms as thick as telegraph poles. He wore a white apron and on his head was a straw boater. He too could entertain and draw in passing trade.

'I went to York for me pork, The Lakes for me steaks, Deal for me veal, and I won't tell ya what I went to Diss for, missis!' The ladies would shriek with laughter.

'Oooh, you are a one, Lester,' chuckled an old lady as she dried her eyes.

In those days of prejudice and homophobia, Lester would reply, 'One o' them love?' as he put one arm on his hip. 'I'm not one o' them, ducky, ask the wife!' Dreadful, I know, but once more, the old lady and her companions would roar with laughter at such atrocious words.

Christmas time was the busiest period of the year. This was when traders made their money. Many wore Father Christmas hats. Some of the more extrovert stall-holders dressed up as snowmen or elves. Sammy wore a large Father Christmas hat with a long piece of wire dangling forwards above his head. On the end was a sprig of mistletoe allowing him to beg a kiss from each female customer.

'Oooh, you are cheeky, Sammy,' said an eighty-year-old lady. 'But you're a lovely kisser. I feel like buying me spuds one at a time!' Such a riposte even made the normally sanguine Sammy speechless.

After Christmas not many people had money to spend and this marked a low time of trading for market people. Weather too dictated how much money a market trader would make. Nobody wanted a downpour. It killed trade.

Everyone on the market worked long hours. When Lenny first started, he had a horse and cart that he used to transport his stock to market. By 1955 he purchased an old van that he joked was kept together with chewing gum and elastic bands. He used the starting handle to turn the engine over. His day started at 4 a.m. and he would return home by 8 p.m. Whilst trading, he was never seen without a mug of tea, freshly brewed by Nora or one of his lads. The cold weather saw him wear black woollen fingerless mittens that still gave him unbelievable dexterity as he picked up and tossed around his goods to his audience. He was a showman, and a good one at that.

Lenny purchased his goods from wholesale warehouses. Some was bankrupt stock and some bought as 'seconds' from factories. Once he bought five boxes of galoshes that he joked were flood damaged. Only two members of his captive audience appreciated this quip.

Lenny had left school at the age of thirteen, yet his maths was as sharp as that of a rent man. His use of the English language was masterful. He possessed a wealth of adjectives and descriptors to vend his wares. His alliteration would have made him a close rival to Leonard Sachs in years to come.

The aisles between the rows of stalls would teem with people on a Friday or Saturday. They were mostly women wishing to spend a portion of the family wage before it had all gone by Monday. Pigeons trotted awkwardly across these aisles on less busy days and seemed unafraid of people as they cut across their path. By the end of the day the walkways were strewn with bits of cardboard and paper. You could always tell when you were approaching the wet fish stall for two reasons. First, was the unpleasant odour of its North Sea produce; the smell would grab you by the throat. Secondly, the loud cries of Beryl Heggarty, fishmonger extraordinaire, would hack its way through the piscatorial atmosphere. She had a loud voice and a personality to match.

'Gorra nice bit of 'ake for ya love. Fresh from Fleetwood this mornin', flower. One and tuppence. Feed the whole family that will. What d' ya think?'

Old Ronnie Vincent was a blind accordion player who always stood at one end of the main market aisle. Market inspectors allowed him to remain without him paying a pitch fee. He lost his sight through shrapnel from a shell exploding in his trench, two days before the Armistice. Ronnie's dog would dutifully sit alongside him and listen to his limited squeezebox repertoire. 'Roses of Picardy' was back to back with 'Mademoiselle from Armentières'. Cold January mornings played havoc with his fingers and made 'Pack Up Your Troubles In Your Old Kit Bag' almost incomprehensible. His old tin helmet acted as receptacle for penny and halfpenny pieces.

'Casuals' were people who did not have a permanent registered pitch. Some paid on a daily basis if there was a stall available. Others were fly pitchers and worked out of a suitcase or from a trolley. They always had a look out who'd stand like a meerkat scouring the crowd for market inspectors or policemen. They would operate away from the registered pitches and the marketers would tell them in no uncertain terms where they could go. Their advice usually ended in 'off'.

The Cattle Market pub was just around the corner from the market site, and had a special licence to open early for the market men. Some hardened souls supped a pint of best bitter at six in the morning. The landlord would lay on bacon and sausage butties for breakfast, and tempting meat and potato pies for lunch, or dinner as it was called.

The school board man or truancy officer was a frequent visitor to the Flat Iron market. It was usually a Mr Snodgrass who would cruise the alleyways in search of young truants. Lads would take time off to assist their dads, and many would rush to the market after school to help their parents pack away. In those days there was little health and safety guidance as to how long a youngster was permitted to work. Some had to set up the stall before school started and then re-join their dad to close the stall late afternoon. Mr Snodgrass was easily recognised. He was a tall gentleman of six feet, six inches. To add to his altitude he sported a brown trilby. A brown gabardine raincoat and a shiny briefcase completed his uniform. Mr Snodgrass had a long nose and at its tip hung a stubborn dew drop. It was always there, even on a roasting summer's day. Traders knew him, and indeed he knew them. A rehearsed system of warning cries went along the stalls when he came into view. Lester Boothroyd's son was always on the stall, heaving huge, lumbering carcasses of meat. The market telegraph reached the Boothroyd pitch and his son Gordon would hide under the tarpaulins. Mr Snodgrass was advised by Lester that his son had moved away with his mother following a domestic, and it was too upsetting for him to discuss it.

'They've moved to Scotland, I believe,' Lester replied as he wiped his eyes. 'Now, if you don't mind, I find this too emotional to discuss.' The ruse backfired when Mrs Snodgrass was served with a pound of sausages by Gordon, the day after.

On a trading day, most pitches were being set up at 6 a.m. Lenny had to build his theatre with the help of his two lads. He'd already decided what items he was going to sell and had schooled his two apprentices as to the order of sales. By 8 a.m. the stall was ready and it was time for a spot of breakfast. Bacon and egg butties were washed down with a mug of tea. A small primus stove boiled the water that went straight into the mug along with the loose tea. A bottle of milk was kept in a bucket of water with a damp tea towel over the top. It was a simple physics principle about heat exchange and it worked. His lads would complain about the tea leaves and remove them from their tongue as they quaffed the piping hot beverage.

By 8.30 a.m., the first trickle of punters arrived at the market. Some came earlier on their way to work. His sons knew what was expected of them. One would restock and worked at the back of the stall, the other was out front to take money and pass on the purchased goods. All three wore an apron that had a pocketed zip. Any notes were passed to dad who was behind the stall for security reasons. All three had a float consisting of threepenny bits, sixpences, shillings, half crowns, ten bob and pound notes. Dad had the fivers.

By around 9.30 a.m. the first wave of customers settled around his stall. Lenny had drawn them in with loud cries of, 'Here we go then ladies and gentlemen. Come closer love, you'll see the bargains better. Now, who's going to offer me five bob for me first bargain? Come on ladies. Len'll never let you down!'

Slowly three hands were raised.

'Lovely stuff and here's your first deal.' Lenny then held up an empty carrier bag. 'There you are ladies a beautifully fashioned bag. Walk along Deansgate and you'll be the envy of 'em all.'

The hands quickly go down with cries of disappointment.

'Oh dear, I've lost me customers. I'm not gonna rob ya! I tell you what. If I do this, then this, then this, how's that for five bob? Go on ladies I feel generous today I'll even chuck in one of these as well!'

Lenny had stuffed the bag with a bath towel, three pot towels and three flannels and finally a boxed pen. Immediately the hands would go back up and start to wave frantically to catch his attention. The bags would be slung out to the hysterical crowd. The boys would then collect the five bobs.

Lenny's job was to keep the excitement going with his next offering. One bargain was swiftly followed by others. He'd repeat the tactic of selling many things together.

'Now, how about this, ladies? An electric kettle, two pound in the shops. A set of six teaspoons an' all. Look at this carving knife, beautiful for your roast. It'd cut through paper it's that sharp. A set of egg cups, six of 'em! Look, not one, not two, not three, but four bargains.' Lenny would pile these boxes one on top of each other and bang them down to punctuate his words.

'Now look ladies, I'm not asking a fiver for this lot. I'm not asking four. God knows I'm not even asking three quid! Give us two pound ten for the lot! Two pound ten for the lot. I must need my bumps feelin'!' As Len reached his final price crescendo he'd bang on the table and put the goods in a carrier bag and was greeted with another show of eager hands.

'There y'are ladies I'm giving stuff away! You've got good quality stuff there ladies, good quality.' The pound and ten bob notes would then flow into his apron.

Dinner sets were his speciality. He would juggle the plates, shuffle them, and make them fan out like a hand of playing cards. His dexterity was so slick he never damaged one. Another ploy was to say he'd only got two of these items. They were usually more expensive goods such as a kid's racing car or a necklace.

'You'll see 'em for ten pound in the shops in town. I've only got two. It was all I could get hold of. Quality schmatter, there y'are ladies and gents, fiver. Go on give us a fiver?' Another instant sale was predictably followed by two five pound notes in the apron.

The day rolled on with Lenny knocking out string vests, the type worn by Victor Mature. Ladies' nylons direct from a store on the Champs Elysées in Paris. None of his audience had ever visited Paris so they wouldn't know. He also sold a pair of porcelain cats that under normal circumstances would have been put in the bin by most people. His gift of the gab ensured that at least five pairs went to his clientele.

'Two lovely black and white cats here, ladies. Just look at 'em made from the finest china clay. Beautiful! What's that lady? Are they mounted? No, they're just lookin' fondly at each other!'

At Christmas, Eddie Calvert plastic golden trumpets were sold as kids' stocking fillers in abundance, only for them to annoy the family on Boxing Day. It really was 'Oh my papa, to me he was so wonderful.' Although most papas would give the kid a crack round the head and tell him to stop playing that wretched thing!

It was easy money in those days even though his customers didn't have much of it. His hard work allowed him to clear his stock. It was good to arrive home but he still had to visit the lock up to load up for the next day. Nora always had a hot mug of tea ready for him and an evening meal for him and the boys. Lenny then collapsed into an armchair to rest his aching feet.

'Ooooh, me dawgs are killin' me,' he would always say.

Just as he was comfortable there was a cry from the backyard. It was Nora.

'Len? I'm on the lavvy. We've run out o' toilet rolls. Where did you put them boxes this mornin'?'

'I moved 'em like you asked me too, my precious,' he shouted back.

'Well, where did ya move 'em to? I need one now,' she replied.

'I'm sorry my angel but I sold the lot this afternoon! You'll have to use the *Daily Mirror*!'

# The McGowan Family
# at Number 26

A SMALL CROWD OF PASSERS-BY gathered on the pavement opposite
number 26, Copenhagen Street. It was a cold, damp morning in
February. Residents of the street had witnessed police visits to this
house before. A burly sergeant, accompanied by two equally brawny
police constables, was in the process of thumping on the front door of
the McGowan residence.

'I wonder what they've done this time?' tutted Mrs Myrtle Dempsey.

'More like WHO they've done this time,' corrected her neighbour.
'Aye, they'd pinch yer boots and come back for the socks off yer feet
that lot,' she continued.

The McGowan family had lived in the street for just under a year,
though it seemed to everyone an absolute lifetime. They were a family
of seven who had moved to Salford from a tenement in their native
city of Glasgow. They each brought with them an accent you could
cut only with a chain saw. When Mr and Mrs McGowan were arguing
after a night on the booze, their high volume patois sounded like a
miscellany of German, Icelandic and Gaelic. However, they both
seemed to understand each other, and when he shouted that he was
going to break her jaw, she understood the message and defended
herself by smashing him over the head with a chamber pot. It was
never dull and uneventful living near the McGowans.

The family comprised Archie, the dad, Morag, the mother, and five children aged from two to nineteen. Archie had never been known to work since arriving in Copenhagen Street. Horace Dewhurst, licensee of The Fusilier's, once quipped that one of Archie's national insurance stamps was worth more than a Penny Black. Archie would often be found standing on the front doorstep leaning against the wall. In all weathers he would be seen in an old, torn vest, grubby with age. His trousers were the bottoms of overalls held below his large paunch by a wide leather belt. He always appeared unshaven, and his face bore a jagged scar under the left eye. On occasions when he had shaved, his lower jaw and cheeks bore collections of blood-stained tissue paper. One of his chunky arms was home to a patchwork of unidentifiable tattoos drawn by an untalented and dyslexic back street artist in Govan many years before. Serpents were supposed to intertwine with poorly drawn daggers and hearts. One image bore the word SCOSHA, designed to reflect Archie's national pride. Needless to say the artist received a good pasting from Archie when he viewed the final indelible attempt at the Latin word for Scotland.

Archie was never complete without a roll-up stuck in the corner of his lower lip. When he spoke this cigarette bobbled up and down in sympathy with his incomprehensible dialect.

Morag had married Archie some twenty-five years before when, according to her, he was a fine figure of a man. There was a photograph of their wedding day on the mantelpiece that made them look like a pair of tag wrestlers celebrating a recent victory. She had a face that had seen action. Indeed, her wild and disquieting visage could easily have been a substitute for the skull and cross bones on a poison bottle. She wore the same dress each day, part covered by a 'pinny'. Her bare arms were often bruised from protecting herself from Archie. Her hair was never completely tied back and several of her auburn locks fell awkwardly across her face. Nevertheless, she was more than a match for Archie and could equal his rants and foul language.

The McGowan kids were three boys and two girls. Moira and Ailsa were ten and five years. Both had matted, shaggy hair and a pale, almost colourless complexion. As Mrs Dempsey would say, 'They both look as though they could do with a good dinner down 'em!'

They too had one dress each and it was rumoured they had been sewn into their underclothes when they were toddlers. They were frequently seen bare footed.

Morag's sons were Alistair, Drew and Lachlan. Two-year-old Ali never stopped crying, and in an attempt to silence his wailing, Mrs McGowan would slip gin into his bottle. The poor soul was always seen with a dummy or dodie, and because the comforter was placed next to a bottle of cheap, sweet sherry, its chemistry was also under suspicion.

The other two boys were the oldest of the McGowan crew. Nineteen-year-old Drew was a younger image of his father, quick-tempered, aggressive and totally dishonest. Lachlan, three years younger, was devious, corrupt and totally insensitive. In total, the McGowans were not only a dysfunctional family unit but they also began to cause problems in the local community since their placement in Copenhagen Street in June 1953.

The children didn't easily mix with other kids in the street. The girls would join in with whatever game was being played but soon they would sour proceedings. In skipping games, one of them would lunge at the rope as someone else was skipping. Hopscotch was abandoned as Ailsa would stand in the middle of the squares and refuse to move. 'What's the time, Mister Wolf' finished as Moira would hospitalise Mister Wolf by giving him a real hard thump between the shoulder blades. The girls just found it difficult to mix and the children in the street were scared of their ways.

The McGowan premises were easily distinguishable from the adjacent properties. Most people took pride in their rented houses. Doorsteps and windowsills would be freshly donkey-stoned, often on a daily basis. Net curtains would be hung at parlour windows. Coal holes were swept following the coalman's visit and every fragment of nutty slack coal dust was tidied away. The McGowan house displayed a boarded up parlour window and the upstairs front bedroom window had a diagonal crack that had existed from day one of their tenancy. The steps and windowsills never got a clean and the coalman never called. Instead, Archie and the kids would push a pram down to Patricroft locomotive sheds and pilfer lumps of coal whilst the two young girls distracted the railway workers around the coal tip.

Mrs Dempsey would tell her kids, 'When you walk past the McGowan's house, always hold yer breath!'

It was true, there was always a curious smell emanating from the property. The odour was hard to describe. Someone once said it was a fusion of Bisto and urine. In the summer it changed slightly to an acrid unpleasantness. It was, indeed, quite noticeable and was due to bed bugs. Evidence for their presence chez McGowan was that the two young girls always had bite marks on their arms and legs. Their mother, as triage nurse and apothecary, would daub these sores with Gentian Violet or tincture of iodine.

The farewell remark of 'Move yer bed away from the wall and sleep tight, and mind the bugs don't bite', was particularly relevant at the McGowans'.

When the school nurse asked Mrs McGowan about the bites on her daughter's legs and arms, she would retaliate: 'They don't bite him!' pointing to Archie. I'm not surprised, neither would I.

Another aspect of public health that really precipitated action by neighbours was the sudden rise in cockroach infestations. The landlord eventually gained access to the property and the McGowan house was fumigated with sulphur candles and the noxious spray of sulphuryl fluoride. The two toxic ingredients would be guaranteed to kill everything they fell upon.

'Can't you fumigate *them* at the same time?' Mrs Dempsey asked one of the workmen. The McGowans were asked to vacate their house during the fumigation process.

Archie's predilection for alcohol caused him to be rapidly barred from The Fusilier's. He punched two of Horace's regulars in a row over a horseracing bet. Instead he patronised the Craven Heifer until his bar tab remained unpaid. Archie finally parted company with this establishment one Sunday lunchtime, when he became over-flirtatious with a customer's wife. The problem seemed to resolve itself when it took six men to throw him out onto the street. An unintelligible sentence then emerged from Archie's lips:

'Wat's the mat? Wat's the ma wi' you Jam?'

Archie was finally dragged home by both Drew and Lachlan. His face was bloodstained and his brain sodden with alcohol. The lady to whom Archie had made amorous advances shouted to Gloria the barmaid, 'Who was that bugger, anyroad? He pounced on me like a cow on heat!'

'You mean bull on heat, don't ya?' corrected Gloria.

'Well, ya know what I mean. He had a face like an angry boil ... and where was he from anyroad? I couldn't understand 'im. Was he one o' them southerners, or what?'

Some of Archie's money came from occasional, cash in hand, labouring jobs but mainly he was a thief and his two older sons saw him as Fagin, dropping them a few bob for their exploits. There is a code amongst thieves that you don't do it on your own doorstep. Archie and his siblings rejected this protocol and frequently robbed from families in the street. Milk would disappear from doorsteps. Galvanised baths would vanish from backyards. Shirts and trousers would go, and woe betide the family who hung out their Sunday best. Indeed, Archie was once seen wearing Mr Dempsey's new shirt, reserved for Sunday mass. Mr Dempsey thought twice about demanding its return.

Most people left a front door key on a piece of string on the inside of the front door, being accessible if you put your hand through the letterbox. Practices like this ceased shortly after the McGowans moved in. Local residents would break glass and cement its shards on the top of the walls around the backyard to keep out the McGowans.

Along the row of houses where the McGowans lived, a sudden rash of thefts took place. The police and the tenants could not work out the *modus operandi* of these burglaries. The McGowans were suspected by all, using the rationale that they would nick anything that wasn't nailed down or cemented in. A silly mistake made by Drew led to the discovery of the mechanism of these robberies. Archie sent Drew into the loft in search of anything that had been left by the previous tenants, only for him to discover there was a common loft space that ran the full length of this row of terraced houses. The agile larcenist was then dispatched over a period of weeks along the loft, and he would drop into neighbouring properties via the loft hatch, when they were out.

The series of thefts concluded when an overzealous Drew decided to burgle the Mancini family, six doors down. Mr Mancini had papered over the loft hatch and as the cunning young Glaswegian pulled up the Mancini loft hatch, he took half the ceiling paper with him. Copenhagen Street waved goodbye to Drew shortly after this ceiling paper stripping exercise, as he was admitted to a Borstal for young offenders. To reduce his sentence he asked for seven other loft hatches to be taken into consideration.

Because the family had relocated many times over their years in Scotland, a school education for their children was a low priority. In

Copenhagen Street, the School Board man was a frequent visitor and was quickly sent on his way by Mr or Mrs McGowan. One such visit left Mr Cyril Batty, the school attendance and welfare officer, covered in urine as a hung over Morag emptied the contents of last night's potty over him. He left saying they would hear from the education authority about this, to which Mrs McGowan shouted, 'Aye bring 'em on Jim, and they'll gee a taste o' pess an' all!'

Financial penalties to them didn't matter. They had nothing so they couldn't lose anything. The only threat that seemed to worry Morag was the possibility of her kids being taken into care. At the height of one of these threats, and Morag's stubborn brinkmanship, she would finally back down and offer some olive branch to temporarily pacify the authorities.

One of Morag's favourite scams was to purchase a loaf from the baker and slip a slither of glass into it when she got home. She would return the loaf and with a dramatic performance worthy of an Ibsen play. She would be paid off with cakes or money in an effort to prevent her reporting the shop to health and safety inspectors. Morag did the rounds of local shops with this ploy until she was finally rumbled. Bessy Mulvaney, proprietor of a tripe and cow-heel emporium off Greengate, shouted at her as she tried it on once more, 'I remember you doing this last year ya scruffy madam. Now, bugger off from my shop before I leather ya with this!' Bessy picked up a string of black puddings and swung them around her head rather like a Viking king would swing his axe. Morag thought twice about challenging this large-proportioned, black-pudding-wielding woman, and ran out of the shop empty handed.

Buying 'on tick' was a shopping practice beyond the McGowan family. Putting the purchase 'in the book' or 'on the slate' was a process reserved for a few reliable and trustworthy families. The McGowans' reputation as poor payers and unscrupulous citizens spread through the local community like an influenza virus. Archie's talents as an electrical engineer were clearly illustrated when he tried to by-pass the meter. He had done well in Scotland, being the only person in the tenement block whose meter contained no money at all when the man came to empty it. Archie would tower over the meter man as he opened the empty box and not a shilling in sight.

'We just don't feel the cold, son, and I work nights. No need for the leccy, ya see!' he would say.

The rent man too would seldom have luck on his Friday visit. He would thump on the door to no avail. In desperation he would lift the letterbox and shout to the kids inside, 'Come on kids, get yer mother to the door. I want the rent!' It was as if the family inside was of Chinese pedigree because they would return his call with cries of, 'Shintin! Shintin!'

The household was incomplete without Archie's whippet. This mangy representative of the canine world would often win him a few bob at illegal whippet racing in the local park. Archie described the dog's physique as fine-tuned and lean. Others would use different descriptors such as 'starving', and when Archie picked up the mutt, he looked as though he was carrying a xylophone. The dog had no lead, just a piece of rope around its neck. The sight of Archie off to races was reminiscent of Bill Sikes and his trusty Bullseye. He was eventually barred from this event when Archie was found feeding the poor animal Benzedrine obtained from Mrs McGowan. At Archie's request she visited the GP with tales of woe and returned with a prescription for 'Mothers' Little Helpers', which then were fed to the dog on race day. On one occasion Jocky the whippet was so pilled up, he carried on running to Bolton.

The police were frequent visitors at the McGowan abode. They would always arrive in threes. It was rare to catch Archie at home, and Morag would shout to them in broad Glaswegian, as they hammered on the front door, 'Eees no en! No en, I tell ya! Noo pess off and lee us alone.'

People would slow down as they passed by. Neighbours would peer from behind their net curtains. On one particular February morning a visit from the local gendarmerie was greeted with nil response, as usual.

A sudden shout from the crowd of onlookers solved the cold calling mystery for the policemen:

'They've done a moonlight! A moonlight flit. I saw him with an horse and cart last night.'

Flitting was slang for moving house. A moonlight flit was practised by a family who found itself weeks in arrears with the rent. A sudden decision was made to move all their possessions to another house under cover of darkness. It was an attempt to vanish without trace.

'Well, good riddance to bad rubbish!' shouted Mrs Dempsey, 'Street'll be a lot better without 'em, an' all.'

And, do you know? It was.

# The Barlow Family
## at Number 17

'Is that you, our Eddie?' shouted Mrs Barlow. 'Only, I'm upstairs making the beds.'

'No, it's me, mam. I'm going to go with you this morning. I'll make sure he sorts you out,' replied Freda, her daughter.

'I thought Eddie were coming to fix the cistern in the lavvy?' enquired Mrs Barlow.

'He is mam, but he's comin' after work. I'm going to the doctor's with you. It's about time that chest of yours was sorted. It's been going on for too long, all this wheezing and coughing,' called Freda.

Ida Barlow was born at home in Tooley Street, in 1898. Her parents, Jack and Mona, had two other children. It was an age when Manchester was nicknamed 'Cottonopolis', and across its trading floors, millions of pounds were exchanged during the boom years. Cotton was king, and the cotton mills and the pits of Lancashire worked with a synergy to make their proprietors wealthy and influential people.

One such mill owner was Sir Elkanah Armitage who, by the mid 1800s, had built mills in Pendleton and Patricroft. His lifetime connection with cotton, together with an eye for an opportunity, made him site these two mills next to water and the railway. The River Irwell would provide the steam generated by huge boilers to drive the machinery, and the coal from the local pits of Pendleton and Agecroft was the source of chemical energy. The town was also blessed with engineering works turning out parts for loom mechanisms. The cotton industry in this area was, indeed, self-sufficient.

Elkanah's New Mill in Pendleton employed 600 people. This factory, plus the Victoria Mill in Patricroft, boasted 80,000 spindles and over 2,000 looms. These figures contributed to Lancashire's cotton supremacy in these times, for in 1860, the county showed 1,920 registered mills.

Ida and her two sisters followed their mother into employment at New Mill. Kids joined the mill workforce at the tender age of fourteen and started work at 7 a.m. and finished at 5 p.m. There was one hour for lunch and a ten-minute tea break in the morning. Adults would start earlier at 6.30 a.m. and be given a breakfast break. The work you did was according to your aptitude, how quickly you could learn new skills. The best money was to be made as a loom operator; the more looms you ran, the better your wages. Piece work meant you were paid on the amount of weaving your looms achieved.

The workforce in New Mill, like all mills in the area, was predominantly female. Sixty-five per cent of the 575,000 mill operatives in Lancashire were women.

Ida joined the New Mill ladies in September 1912 and was given training for three months. It wasn't just the simple theory of the weft and the warp of the weaving process she had to quickly assimilate, it was to understand the process and science of the looms, and all their individual idiosyncrasies. Simple procedures like knot tying were reinforced with more complex operations such as replacing one shuttle with another to maintain continuity and what to do when the weft breaks to produce a flawless end product. Ida was trained by Vera Morris, a lady who wore a white coat that highlighted her role, and separated her from the shop floor workforce. Vera was a bright lady who also doubled as the first aider and triage nurse. Ida would praise Vera for her patience and understanding of the new recruit's naivety and innocence.

One important piece of guidance given to her by her workmates was to never upset the tacklers. The tacklers were men dressed in dark blue overalls who sat in an office at the entrance to the weaving shed. They were seen as rude and arrogant men. Their job was to keep the looms moving and to repair and maintain machinery. They were always old blokes and many had a misogynistic and insensitive persona. During her early apprenticeship, Ida soon discovered that mistakes she made cost the company money, and the tacklers certainly let her know of their misgivings in respect of her ability to weave.

'Does tha' 'ead button up the back, ya stupid lass?' was one of the first verbal assaults she received from one such tackler.

However, Ida did notice that the more experienced, older female workers gave them back as good as they got.

'Never mind cursin' me Albert Barnes, just get that bloody belt drive workin', I'm losin' money here, 'cos o' you!' shouted Lilly Phillips, a weaver of over thirty years' experience. The sullen Mr Barnes thought twice about challenging this seasoned veteran, and did what she commanded as quickly as possible.

Ida's sisters started in the blowing and carding rooms. If Ida thought the weaving sheds were dusty then her sisters would tell her otherwise. Clouds of cotton dust would hang defiantly in the air, and the tall windows would allow sunlight to pick out the white particulate haze. Health and safety, despite Factory Act legislation, was still a low priority. The cotton industry was driven by profit and not on humanitarian principles. The wearing of face masks only happened in the late 1940s and was not compulsory. Many women refused to wear them because, 'They get in your way, and breathing is hard enough at the best of times'. At the end of the day, throats were dry and lungs were full. Some women pleaded that a few Woodbines helped shift the stuff, but long-term exposure to the fibrous fluff made many victim of 'Cotton Lung' – a less alarming term for byssinosis, a form of emphysema.

The cotton dust had also been a problem relating to fire for many years, particularly when the lighting of the mill was by gas lamps. Sparks from machines or clogs on the bare stone floors could easily precipitate explosions strong enough to shatter windows and blow people off their feet. Primitive sprinkler systems connected to shallow tanks on the roof allowed gravity to do its job and extinguish any blaze.

Lubricants, necessary to smooth the movement of metal on metal, were poured onto the moving parts. Their bearings and rotating shafts would fire a toxic vapour of oil that mixed with the moist air. The resulting miasma was a powerful carcinogenic potion that could lead to mule spinners' cancer. Women discovered these noxious fumes targeted their lips, whilst male workers were vulnerable to scrotal carcinomas. Dermatitis and eye infections were common and completed the mill worker's pathology menu.

The weaving shed was a single-storey long room with whitewashed walls, and north-facing roof lights. The shed consisted of row upon row of identical looms, inches apart. These looms were powered by leather belts, and ran from overhead cross-shafts. A long line-shaft stretched the length of the mill and bevel gears would transmit the power to these cross-shafts. Very few guards were found along these transmissions.

Ida wore a cotton 'pinny'. The heat and humidity in the weaving sheds, even on a winter's day could be unbearable. Humidity ran at eighty five percent and condensation would teem down the cold stone walls. These atmospheric conditions were necessary to maintain the quality of the spun yarn and stop it from breaking. A fent, acting like a gater, was deemed compulsory for all loom operatives, and was a piece of cloth around the waist to stop clothes becoming snagged in this unforgiving and unprotected machinery. Therefore, ladies wore short-sleeved dresses. Many wore headscarves, knotted at the front. Most women operated four looms from a narrow space, with two looms in front of them, and two behind. Cotton fibres accumulated on the floor between the looms and old blokes would sweep the spaces to prevent fire.

Ida didn't want to copy her mother. Her mum wore clogs that clanked across the stone floors. Instead she wore her school shoes. Boot and shoemakers in the locality specialised in clogs whose soles were hammered in with nails. The toes and heels of this footwear were strengthened with metal tips and caused sparks along the stone floors and so it was essential these cotton fibres were swept away. Clogs were seen as sensible and practical, hardwearing footwear. Before Ida started at the mill she would listen to the factory hooter sound at 5 p.m. and then hear the clack, clack noise of hundreds of clogs thumping against scarred pavements, as people squeezed through the mill gates on their way home. Women in shawls, men in cloth caps would clatter across cobbled streets eager to escape from a day's hard labour at the mill.

Ida's mother and father, along with other families in the street also employed by the mill, had the services of a 'knocker up'. This ageing soul would rap on the front bedroom window with a long cane. The cane had a screw tied to it with a piece of string. Its vibrations against the glass would wake the dead, according to her father. It certainly didn't wake Mr Cyril Webster of number twenty-five, a notorious toper whose daily nightcap was eight pints of Holt's bitter at the Craven Heifer. Mr Webster was a grinder at the mill and was a huge block of a man. Grinders operated with brawn not brain. They hauled enormous bales of cotton and worked behind the machinery. Sadly, Cyril's habitual late arrival at the New Mill soon cost him dearly. His tardiness forced him to part company with the mill payroll and forfeit his job.

One of the first things Ida experienced was the incessant, deafening noise of the looms. Their tireless chitter-chatter resonated against the stone slab floors. Communication between loom operators was almost impossible when the machines were running. Shuttles in a 500 loom shed were being thumped at over two hundred times a minute. Women were skilled in lip reading and mee-mawing, where words were exaggerated by labial contortions supplemented with sign language. Nobody wore ear protectors; they were unheard of, and so deafness and tinnitus were common side effects of the job. A quick visit to the toilet – and it had to be quick – meant signalling to a neighbouring worker, and for her to keep an eye on your looms.

Conversations were only possible at lunchtime, known as dinner. Many of the female workforce would go home because they had to complete their own domestic chores. In Ida's day there was no canteen at the mills. This facility came in during the 1940s and was supplied by local pie shops and bakeries. Male employees would often play football in the yard after they'd finished their butties. The morning tea break saw the workforce drinking black tea from mugs encrusted with years of brown tannin. Nobody had milk in their tea because the hot working conditions meant the milk quickly soured even if the bottle of milk had been placed in a bucket of cold water with a damp tea towel over its top. There were no teapots to brew the tea, instead the raw tea was spooned into your mug and then stirred in the boiling water from the kettle. This made the final few slurps a tricky undertaking if you didn't want to be spitting tea leaves for the rest of the morning.

It took a while for Ida to make friends at the mill. Most of her working colleagues were middle aged with husbands and families. So, life was rather dull for her in those early years. Ida was sixteen at the start of the Great War. Many of the men at the local mills enlisted, for much of their work was not classed as a reserved occupation. The male population of the district dropped sharply over those four bloody years of conflict. Men from the Lancashire Fusiliers, incorporating the Salford Pals, together with members of the Manchester Regiment, suffered huge losses. The Salford Pals regiment was almost wiped out at Thiepval Ridge on The Somme on 1 July 1916.

Towards the end of the war, a girl named Mavis Greenwood arrived at the mill. She was four years older than Ida, and lived in Canal Street around the corner from Ida's mum and dad. They soon struck up a good friendship and would meet up and natter on their way to and from the mill. Mavis worked as a winder and her job in the winding room, in a separate building three floors above Ida's weaving shed, was to wind thread onto the spindles used in shuttles.

Ida was now twenty, and though most of her wages went to her mum for her keep, she had saved up during those apprentice years to buy herself new shoes, a 'going out dress' and some makeup. She and Mavis would go to the picture house and often visit the Woolpack pub. It was there the two girls met a couple of brothers, Sam and Billy Barlow. Billy was a colliery fitter at Agecroft pit and had a certified or reserved occupation as it was later called. His brother Sam was not so fortunate. He worked as a bookbinder off Cheetham Hill and was called up in 1916. Sam was gassed at Pilckem Ridge in the Third Battle for Ypres in 1917 and never kept good health from that time onwards. The couples started going out and Ida took a real shine, as her mother would say, to Sam.

It was soon big news at the mill that Ida was 'courting', and she in particular was often the butt of banter from the rest of the ladies.

'Is he a good kisser, Ida?'

'Does he 'old yer 'and when he takes you out, love? Make sure that's the only thing he 'olds, Ida!' shouted the demonstrative Mrs Lilly Phillips. The comments were hardly intrusive but would quickly make Ida blush.

The women at the mill were hard, and had to be. They were capable of working long hours in oppressive conditions and were then expected to run a house and perform their domestic duties. Even though there was a toughness and resilience among these women there was also a sense of camaraderie. They would show care and concern if one of their work colleagues was distressed. Problems such as bereavement, sickness in the family, separation and infidelity of husbands would all be treated with the same compassion. Ida stated that you never felt as though you had to shoulder problems on your own and that there was always someone there who had lived through and had coped with similar troubles. Even though some of these women could swear and blaspheme for their country, there was still a sense of togetherness and comradeship.

Sam proposed to Ida in September 1922 and they both saved to marry in August 1925. The weaving shed was decorated with bunting on the day before her wedding. Ida was flooded with cards and good wishes from her colleagues. Even the outspoken Mrs Lilly Phillips sent her a card complete with the verse 'Take a tip from one who knows, and tie your nightie to your toes – have a lovely day, kid. You deserve happiness!' Lilly always gave sound practical advice to all brides-to-be. When young loom operator Madge Mason was about to get hitched, and seemed concerned about having something old and new but nothing borrowed and blue, the ever-resourceful Lilly came to her assistance.

'Borrowed and blue?' she enquired. 'How about yer pawn ticket and yer varicose veins love? Job done.'

Ida and Sam moved in with Sam's parents after the wedding, for three years until their two children, Eddie and Freda were born. During those years Ida continued working at the mill and Sam at the bookbinders.

Their new family size saw them move to Gardener Street, a two up two down mid-terraced house, complete with scullery, cellar and an outside lavvy.

The phosgene and chlorine cocktails that Sam had received during the Battle of Ypres courtesy of the German Fourth Army, rendered him debilitated, often for prolonged periods. Severe respiratory problems coupled with blistered skin caused Sam to have time off work and so it was necessary for Ida to continue at the mill. Her mother looked after the children and Ida would run home at lunch to do some domestic chores.

Sadly, by 1935, Sam's physical condition had worsened, and the complication of him losing his sight meant work was now impossible.

Sam suffered continuous respiratory distress and tragically died the following year, leaving Ida alone to lead the family unit. Claiming a military pension at that time was not always an easy process. Sam had died resulting from chronic pulmonary obstructive disease or emphysema as we know it today. She also attributed his skin lesions and poor eyesight to him being gassed. The stumbling block for Ida was that Sam died almost twenty years after his wartime injuries. After much form filling and bureaucratic nonsense, the War Pensions Ministry finally agreed to grant her a weekly pension of twenty six shillings and eight pence. However, this was not backdated. Some war widows had to fight long and hard to receive a military pension.

The years after Sam's death saw Ida still working long hours at the mill but after the Second World War the volume of work decreased due to the onset of cheap cotton goods being available from Asia and the Middle East. It wasn't just the mills around Manchester that were on short time. Mill towns around Burnley, Blackburn and Oldham started to experience the slow drip of closure. Finally, in 1958 the Elkanah mills shut down their looms and cotton spinning ceased.

Ida's children avoided the mill, and Eddie worked on the buses whilst Freda gained employment as a waitress at the Midland Hotel in Manchester. Both had married but Freda called round to see her mother each day at the same time.

'I'm not taking no for an answer, mam. Yer goin' and that's it!' called Freda. 'Now, get yer coat on.'

Ida came down stairs removing her pinny. She took her coat from the peg in the hall.

'I don't know what all the fuss is about, Freda. My cough always gets worse in the winter. A dose of Liquifruita and a mustard plaster on me chest, always does me good,' retorted Ida as she slipped on her shoes.

'Mustard plasters, mam? They're as old as the hills them things! A waste o' mustard, rubbish they are! You need some of that new stuff, ya know? Ask him for that antibiotic stuff.'

'Well, our Freda, we'll wait and see what he says,' Ida answered.

Entering Dr McNamara's consulting room you stepped back in time. Its Victorian décor tended to complement his outdated prescriptions and remedies. His balding pate was flanked by long bushy sideburns that allowed his stethoscope tubing to become lost in them. His waxed collar pinched his adipose neck and the fatty tissue spilled over its margins. This neck-wear was so tight that when he spoke, the knot on his tie moved up and down with each word. His dated, wool, pinstripe suit must have sat opposite patients for some fifty years. People wondered why there was always a Bunsen burner alight on a table next to his long mahogany desk. What was its use? Did he burn parts of your body with it? I eventually discovered he would test urine with it for diabetes by boiling it with Benedict's reagent, a far cry from the biometric testing done today.

Dr McNamara, known as Dr Crippen by his patients, would give you a thorough physical examination without leaving his leather Chesterfield chair. You were summoned to come around the table and stand next to him. Should you need to lie down on his examination couch he would move across to you on castors, still seated.

Ida and her daughter saw Dr McNamara. A consultation with this gentleman was usually a brief experience, and indeed after five minutes they left the surgery with the news that her lung condition was incurable. He gave her a list of the 'do's and 'don't's but rather coldly informed her that it would worsen with time. The Clean Air Act of 1956 would arrive too late, and the pessimistic forecast from this tired physician was, indeed, quite accurate and Ida's health would deteriorate over the following three years.

Our lady mill worker at number six developed acute bronchitis in the winter of 1955 during a prolonged episode of smog. The word smog is a *portmanteau* of the words smoke and fog. The toxic chemical composition of the smoke along with the cold, dank atmosphere would do nothing but aggravate the lungs of the inhabitants of the city whose diet was far short of today's five a day. Indeed, many families never knew where the next meal was coming from. The bread line was a standard out of reach for many. It was, therefore, a black irony at this time when the Right Honourable Harold Macmillan MP informed them they had never had it so good. Ida Barlow passed away three months later aged fifty-nine years.

# The Birdsall Family at Number 16

THEY'D RECEIVED THREE SIMILAR LETTERS before. It was just the names that were different. This one, like all of the others boldly stated:

'We are pleased to inform you that your son Kenneth has passed the Eleven Plus Examination, and this entitles him to a place at the local grammar or technical school. You have until April 16th of this year to reply to this letter stating your preference. Should you not wish to take up one of these placements, then please notify us at the education offices as soon as possible.'

Kenny's three elder brothers had also been successful with that examination but Mrs Dora Birdsall declined the opportunity to enrol her sons because she couldn't afford the uniform. This, and all the extras they would need to be given the opportunity to study such alien subjects as Latin and Physics, was beyond their fiscal remit.

'I don't know where they get their brains from, I tell ya,' professed Dora to one of her neighbours. 'It certainly doesn't come from me, and definitely not from their dad. He thinks algebra is a town in North Africa near where he fought with the Desert Rats.'

Dora made the decision that Kenneth would go to grammar school, particularly now that two of her four sons were bringing home a regular wage. Such a bold decision alarmed her husband, Ted.

'He doesn't need his head filling with dates in history and learning them words in French. The only good thing that's come out o' France is French polishing. Now, there's money in that,' reasoned Ted. His pessimism was beaten down by Dora's persistence. She was proud of the potential shown by all her sons, and at long last wanted something to brag about.

'Does that mean I'll have to wear that poncy green blazer and a cap, mam? I'll look a right jessy. All me mates'll take the rise out o' me in a green school cap. I'm not goin'!' Kenny concluded.

'You are goin', our Kenneth!' exclaimed Dora, and he went.

The grammar school was led by head teacher Reginald 'Boggy' Marsh, a Cambridge graduate in Classics who wished to staff his school also with Oxbridge men. Indeed, there were several light and dark blue varsity men. However, he was forced to accept lesser qualified staff to run the PE, Art and Handicraft departments. 'Boggy' was once overheard saying he would really want to employ these teachers as instructors as they were as close to academia as a plumber or rugby league footballer. His paranoia about PE was justified when 'Boggy' asked a newly qualified PE teacher about his thoughts on a *victor ludorum* on sports day. The young and eager Corinthian replied that the boy was not in his group but he would find out.

It was a boys' grammar school, and the presence of women teachers in his place of learning was unheard of. The only females allowed within the grounds of the school were the two ladies in the school office plus the kitchen staff. The school nurse visited on occasions to check for nits and to check that young testicles defied gravity when their owners were asked to cough. Young Kenny, now a first-year pupil, lined up with thirty of his fellow students outside the medical room. The boy in front of him spied this corpulent lady in a blue uniform, rummaging through kids' hair further up the queue. As the reader will know, it was 'Nitty Nora – The Bug Explorer'. He turned to Kenny and asked him what she was doing, and with true Birdsall wisdom and confidence, Kenny replied, 'She's checkin' if you've got any brains!'

Mr Marsh was a traditionalist and ran the school like a Roman general. Indeed, the main ingredient of his educational philosophy was to rule by fear. He would terrify the kids, and the staff knew never to upset him. The head of PE forfeited his job when he failed to do his sums, and left one of the under-fifteen cricket team in Scotland after a heavy night, celebrating the last match of the tour. He not only lost his job but also suffered an hour-long castigation by Mr Marsh. He was forced to pay the coach fare to reunite the marooned soul in Aberdeen with his parents. That same teacher was no loss to the school. He was a sadist and would slipper a whole class when they seemed reluctant to enter the sub-zero showers.

Kenny hated PE, and so too did an overweight lad in his class. The boy's name was Christopher Peter Bacon. Yes, I suppose with a surname like his, it would encourage banter. The boy's nickname was 'Crispy' for obvious reasons. This young man was given fitness exercises to perform by the PE teacher whilst the less rotund members of the group played rugby. He was once put on a rowing machine and told pull on the oars. After several tugs 'Crispy' stopped.

'Come on lad. Get rowing. Get those arms moving, you lazy boy!' shouted the angry PE teacher.

'If it's alright with you sir, I'd prefer to just sit here and drift for a while,' replied Crispy. The request was declined and Crispy received three whacks of the slipper as a prescription for his inactivity.

The school's role model was Harrow School, and even the school song, 'Forty-Years On', was nicked from this establishment. The link between the North London school founded in the 1570s, and this flat-roofed, hastily erected seat of learning in 1956, was a tenuous one. Harrow School boasted zero free school meals whereas Kenny's grammar school had at least thirty on their books. Harrow's construction was blessed by a royal charter from Elizabeth I, whereas Mr Marsh's establishment was opened by His Worship, The Mayor, a retired black pudding knotter from Ancoats. Nevertheless, staff wore gowns and referred to the canteen as the refectory. The head boy was an eighteen-year-old, Derek Bates, who was abnormally hairy for his age. His permanent 'five o'clock shadow' was a good match for the tide marks of the youngsters in his charge. A bold third-year pupil once joked with him and asked, 'Do you comb your wrists every morning, Bates?' The poor humourist received an unceremonious thumping from the hirsute eighteen-year-old. The aggrieved lad decided to retaliate by chalking on the art room wall, 'Derek Bates master bates'. Unfortunately, this unlucky fellow was to receive a caning from Mr Marsh, mainly because of the sentence's poor syntax, rather than its lewd connotation.

The curriculum diet offered to Kenny and his first-year acolytes comprised English, Maths, French, Science, Art, Handicraft, History, Geography, Religious Instruction and PE. This collection of subjects would remain unchanged until the start of the third year when pupils were asked to choose between the Arts and Sciences. During the two foundation years some pupils were selected to join the 'express stream' where they were groomed for academic stardom by taking their 'O'-levels at the end of the fourth year. Unfortunately, Kenny did not make this band of accelerated learners. However, he was removed from Metalwork and placed in the under-subscribed Latin class on the grounds that in a History lesson he described Manchester United's defence as solid as Hadrian's Wall. The irony of such an historical simile was that Kenny thought the bloke who built it was called Adrian and was probably a bricklayer from South Shields.

Kenny's teachers were a mixture of men returning from the Second World War, those having completed their two years of National Service and the lucky ones who had avoided the military. Mrs Birdsall was full of optimism that Kenny would receive top quality teaching. In reality, many of the professors at this establishment were knowledgeable but lacked the sparkle necessary to motivate the kids. The slogan 'Everyone remembers a good teacher' could only be applied to a few in the school. The descriptors of 'inspirational, enthusiastic and motivational' were reserved for only a handful. Kenny's English teacher was as uplifting as carbon dioxide in a balloon. He read Shakespeare with as much emotion as one would if it were a section of the telephone directory. He was obsessed with gerunds, and forced examples of them into every lesson. Kenny's class said they would sooner chew glass than sit through one of his clause analysis and parsing lessons.

Mr Sinhuber had been hurriedly employed as a Geography teacher. Otto Sinhuber was a graduate from the University of Freiburg and had been a former navigator in the Luftwaffe before being shot down over Liverpool and then taken prisoner. He was a genial soul and attempted humour in physical geography lessons. His German wit would allow him to say, 'Now boys, remember, Vinds blow, from high to low, and zat is poetry.' Hardly side-splitting, I know, but as Kenny said, 'Not bad for a German!' It was also rather embarrassing for some of the 'A'-level geography boys, when faced with study of the economics of the coal and steel industry in the north east of England. Herr Sinhuber made comments like 'Consett, I know it vell, I bombed it during ze var.'

However, the boredom disappeared in Ted Worthington's lessons. Ted was an historian and would bring to life battles of the Napoleonic wars. Kids would be glued to his every word as he animatedly described the efforts of Lord Nelson at the Battle of Copenhagen and Wellington at Waterloo. The blackboard glowed with different coloured chalks representing battle lines. He would use questions such as 'Fraser, put yerself in Napoleon's shoes at Austerlitz, what would you have done?' Terry Fraser, a colourless lad who had the physique of a bacterium, gave the honest reply, 'I would have said I shouldn't be there, sir, 'cos like me dad, I've got flat feet and grommets!'

Anyone who failed the end of topic test would be slippered by Ted. This occasion was enjoyed by everyone with the exception of the failures, who were soon to be assaulted by Ted's enormous slipper. It was a size fourteen! Kids sat on their desks to get a better view of the spectacle and chatted like Madame Defarge at a guillotining. Ted

would open the classroom door and take a measured run up like Brian Statham, the Lancashire fast bowler. The punishment concluded with rubber sole contacting adolescent gluteal muscles, and raising them a good foot off the ground. Here endeth the lesson – the lesson being that you should never fail one of Ted's tests.

Kenny had an allergy to pain and made sure he could recite Napoleon's domestic policy to his mum at breakfast. Mrs Birdsall would smile as he rattled off the salient points. She would then give him a hug and turn to her husband and say, 'There y'are, father. That's what a grammar school education can do for you! Napoleon's Domestos policy.'

Any school, whether it is in the state or private sector, will have to deal with bullying. Kenny's grammar school with its male only clientele was no different. It was unfortunate for Kenny that the weekly wash once left him without a school shirt. His mother told him to wear one of his older brother's for that day until she could get his shirts dry for the next day. Reluctantly, Kenny pulled on the only shirt of his brother's he could find. Its collar was pink in colour with a green paisley front.

'I can't wear this to school, mam. All me mates'll take the rise out o' me!' bawled Kenny.

'Shurrup, our Kenneth, we've nowt else unless ya' want to wear my blouse,' came the swift reply.

Kenny did go to school in that shirt but chose to knot his dad's scarf around his neck. Yes, his mates did tease him about the garment, and to add to his misery, he was caned by his housemaster for wearing non-regulation school uniform. Just as Kenny thought things could get no worse, on his way home from school some big lads from St Xavier's secondary modern school caught up with him on Cock Robin bridge. One burly member of that posse shouted to Kenny, 'Eh up kid! Are you one o' them homos wearing that shirt?' Kenny had shouldered enough sarcasm and rebuke about this vestment.

The indignant and quick-witted Kenny retaliated, 'Give us a kiss and I'll tell ya, fatty!'

Now, fatty's mates thought this an excellent riposte and proceeded to explode with laughter. Unfortunately for Kenny, the corpulent youth did not share their view and punched Kenny on the nose. The shirt now had fresh bloodstains, and was returned to his brother by Kenny. His nose was now twice its normal size and throbbed incessantly like a blind cobbler's thumb. Kenny nursed this enlarged proboscis, plus a fat lip, for the next week. From that point on, Kenny showed more of an interest in the weekly wash.

The school was divided into four houses, each with horizontal tutor or form groups. The neighbouring Catholic grammar school named their houses with a loyalty to religious orders of Dominic, Benedict, Carmelite and Cistercian. Kenny's school was forced by the local education authority to title their houses after local historical dignitaries. Hence, Higginbottom, Flanagan, Ollerenshaw and Cohen were attached to pupils when they joined the school. It was interesting to note that the Jewish contingent of the school roll wished to be placed in Cohen House and the lapsed Irish Catholics in Flanagan. Each house was led by a housemaster, and Kenny's was Mr Birkett, i/c Higginbottom house. Big Ron, as the pupils would call him, taught Latin and was as popular as Vlad the Impaler. He would cane anyone who crossed him. It was suspected that even his wife had copped a few lashings for an overdone sausage and mash one evening. It was widely believed that Big Ron hated children. Rumour had it that Ron had a picture of King Herod on the dining room wall at home. Ron referred to pupils as insurgents and treated them dreadfully.

Poor Kenny was once sent to Big Ron with a message from another teacher. He knocked on Ron's office, entered the room and was immediately caned with three on his bottom. Kenny's pleas of innocence were ignored, and when the tearful and sore lad handed Ron the teacher's note, which asked did he want a spare ticket for the United game on Saturday, Big Ron told Kenny he could have that beating 'on account'. Sadly, our Kenny was never in credit.

After morning registration, the school day would start with corporate worship in the assembly hall. Those supernumerary Catholic boys who couldn't get into the Catholic grammar school had instruction with a French teacher, Mr Gascoigne, himself having been taught by the Jesuits in a school in Lyons. Mr Gascoigne would despair at the boys with their broad Lancashire accents. He would complain to the pupils in his classes about their French pronunciation: 'Really boys, this place is becoming more and more like Coronation Street every day.'

The Jewish contingent had a short service in the canteen. They were joined by the Catholics, and were herded into the hall by the head boy, Derek Bates, to hear the notices. The eighteen-year-old werewolf would shout aggressively down the corridor, 'Right, Jewish boys, and get a move on!'

This cohort would then shuffle along the corridor and squeeze into the rear of the hall. It was an anti-Semitic morning ritual carried out with shameful insensitivity and brutality.

Kenny found school assemblies boring. To distil them down they were typically a prayer and a bollocking. Often, notices included who had passed certain tests or examinations. The humiliating thing was that the names of those students who had failed to gain these awards were also announced for their peers to ridicule them afterwards. This was a practice that was not good at raising one's self-esteem.

By accident, other announcements livened up proceedings. At the end of one boring assembly, Kenny and his acolytes learned from the head teacher that the school first eleven would be pinned to the notice-board after morning break. Maybe it was because they had lost four-nil last Saturday?

Another guaranteed showstopper that livened up assemblies was when someone fainted. After the fainter had fallen forward and crashed through three rows of chairs, Mr Marsh would reluctantly dispatch the head boy and a member of staff to drag the unconscious soul out of the hall, to be taken to the medical room. It was reported that Mr Marsh once caned a fainter for being sick on a member of staff's leg moments before tumbling into the aisle. Mr Marsh had an unorthodox perspective on pastoral care and concern for the child's welfare.

Kenny, like the majority of the students, stayed for school dinners. The rule was to get down to the canteen as soon as the bell sounded. There was never enough cutlery, so boys would grab their knife, fork and spoon and spit on them, to prevent others stealing these utensils. Seven boys would sit at a table under the supervision of a house prefect. This responsible fellow was to ensure everyone had equal portions of food served up from the tureens. Derek Fagan, an extremely intelligent fifth-form pupil who was destined to read English at Durham, once sent his school dinner back to the ladies in the school kitchen. The plate was composed of tough, un-chewable cabbage and swede with the texture of floor sweepings from a saw mill. He included a note that said, 'With deepest sympathy.'

For this act of bravery Derek received a pre-varsity flogging from

Mr Marsh. Young Fagan was seen as a martyr by the rest of the boys for his act of defiance.

Much emphasis was placed on extra-curricular activities. Pupils were expected to undertake the Duke of Edinburgh Award Scheme that involved service to the public, a personal challenge, and a survival weekend. Ged Morris was an habitual truant and his personal challenge was to get to school on time. For Philip Norton's service to the public he decided to visit an old person's home and see them across a busy road outside these premises. The school received a telephone call from the home saying the overzealous Philip was taking people across the road when all they wanted was to sit in their armchair and read the newspaper. Kenny couldn't think of a personal challenge so his music teacher persuaded him to learn the double bass. Sadly, Kenny's mastery of this instrument lasted only four hours because the bus conductor wouldn't let him on the bus carrying the said piece.

'Yer not gerrin' on my bus with that thing. It's a safety hazard. That spike nearly had me eye out!' he concluded. I wonder how Julian Lloyd Webber managed with his cello?

Four pupils, including Kenny, did their survival weekend in Derbyshire and were supposed to hike and then camp on the hills outside Matlock. The team gave up walking after a couple of miles and caught the bus the rest of the way. The Duke is still unaware of this dishonesty to this day and the boys are still in possession of their bronze award.

Towards the end of the five years of compulsory secondary education, all students were to receive a careers interview. It was felt by 'Boggy' Marsh that some senior member of staff could conduct these sessions rather than a careers officer supplied by the LEA. Ralph Chadwick, the school's ageing deputy head, fulfilled this role. The trouble was, Ralph was to careers education what Joe Stalin was to social work. Most boys at the school were expected to enter the sixth form and then go off to university. The advisory sessions took place in Ralph's office, which looked as though you could get anything from an A35 gearbox to a coronation mug. Boys were asked to stand in front of his desk whilst they listened to Ralph's sagacious recommendations.

One of Kenny's friends at interview told Ralph he wanted to be a poet. This information shocked Ralph, who then told him that he looked like a doctor.

'Have you thought of medicine, lad?' enquired the deputy head.

'No, sir,' replied the youth.

'Well, at least you are frank, Proctor.'

'No, I'm Barry Proctor, sir.' The reply sailed over Ralph's head.

'We need doctors, you know. A good career too!' Ralph persisted. 'Can I put down that you intend to think about it, Proctor? Yes, Doctor Proctor. Sounds good … Even rhymes. Show the next boy in, will you?'

Kenny's session with Ralph was also over in a flash.

'You know, Birston,'

'It's Birdsall, sir.'

'Yes … You can work indoors or outdoors … You can work with people or on your own. There, I've given you something to think about, Birley.'

'It's Birdsall, sir and I thank you.'

'No problem, lad … Next!'

Despite some rather mediocre teaching, Kenny secured some decent 'O'-levels and expressed a wish to stay on at school to take his 'A'-levels. Mr Birdsall was opposed to the idea, claiming a loss of a wage.

'What good is it going to do him, mother? What good? He's best leaving and getting an apprenticeship at Mather and Platt's. Who knows, in a few years he could be working in the drawing office?' he reasoned, over a Sunday morning cup of tea.

Kenny had informed his mum he wanted to do Maths, Further Maths and Physics. This mystified his dad, who questioned his subject selection.

'What's the two lots o' Maths then, adding up and taking away? I reckon with them skills I could get you in at Micky Finn's the bookie.'

Mrs Birdsall gave her son absolute praise and encouragement. Kenny's older brothers too persuaded him he was doing the right thing. It was good to have such support from his family. Dad was old school, and a dinosaur. However, it was he who was caught bragging in the Fusilier's six years later.

'Oh, he's got everything my son, 'O'-levels, 'A'-levels, spirit-levels. He's been to university. There's nowt he doesn't know about engineering. I taught him all he knows,' he crowed.

'He doesn't know much then Ted!' quipped one of his drinking partners.

Kenny did eventually work at Mather and Platt, the engineering firm, not in the drawing office but as their chief engineer. Mrs Birdsall put it all down to a good grammar school education and Napoleon's Domestos policy.

# Mr Fairclough at Number 35

THEY ALL SAID IT WAS A TRAGEDY, her dying at such a young age. It happened so quickly. Ted had kissed her as he went off to work and three hours later, poor Jennifer was gone. The coroner pronounced it to be sudden arrhythmic death syndrome, a form of heart disease that can lie dormant for years and then strike with merciless, fatal consequences.

Ted and Jennifer had been married for five years.

'Oooh she was a lovely girl, Jennifer. Long, golden hair, always looked neat. She had a lovely figure an' all. Always had time for you. A great shame. It came right out of the blue, this heart thing of hers,' explained Mrs Carrison. 'They were a devoted couple, her and Ted,' she added.

Ted Fairclough worked on the railways as a fireman. He'd been a railway man since leaving school, starting as a cleaner in the local sheds. His ambition was to become a driver but this responsibility would mean a long apprenticeship as a fireman. The fireman's job was to ensure the locomotive was fully operational, and then on the footplate to maintain a good head of steam as the locomotive thundered along on its journey. Firemen also acted as an extra pair of eyes for the driver.

He met Jennifer at secondary school, and after plucking up enough courage, he asked her to go with him to Amy Goodall's dance studio above Burtons the tailors on Broad Street. They were both seventeen at that time and eagerly participated in Amy's lessons for four years. During that time, the waltz was followed by the quickstep, and after making a real hash of the slow foxtrot, Ted proposed and Jennifer accepted. Jennifer was working as a pattern maker at Mandleberg's raincoat factory and they eventually married after a long engagement in September 1955.

A job on the railways in those days was a job for life. Most railway men took a pride in their job and the team of cleaners Ted joined, worked hard to ensure that any passenger or goods locomotive leaving the sheds was in pristine condition. Connecting rods, sand pipes and boiler walls had to gleam in the crisp morning air. Coupling rods, pistons and steam pipes must sparkle.

The first day of Ted's cleaning apprenticeship saw him being ordered onto the top of the engine, and asked to clean the chimney. Needless to say, Ted dropped down from the engine as black as night, much to the amusement of his fellow cleaners. He was also on the receiving end of more initiation pranks, such as being asked to collect from the stores a bucket of steam, a tin of elbow grease, and one that really got him in trouble by the charge hand was being told to ask the store man for a long weight. Ted remained at the serving hatch for an hour before the irate supervisor spotted him and dragged him back to his cleaning duties by his ear.

One important inclusion in any rail worker's kit from day one was the British Rail rule book. At stages during his cleaner apprenticeship, Ted was tested on this manual before even being considered for a position as an apprentice fireman. After six long years of cleaning duties, Ted was given the position of part-time fireman. He first worked on goods trains that were less constrained to time schedules than passenger services. It was during this phase of Ted's railway education that he learned his trade and the mechanics of steam engines.

Drivers tended to be 'old blokes' with years of experience. Ted was only in his twenties, and he fed on the wisdom and guidance of these senior colleagues that helped him through those early days of being a fireman. This job would take him many years to become match fit.

Often, firemen had to wait twenty years for consideration for a driving position. It was then, and only then, that he would be deemed suitable for engine driving. Waiting for a suitable driver vacancy was like 'dead men's shoes'.

It was during the early years of Ted's training as a fireman that he lost his wife. He and Jennifer had initially moved into furnished rooms in Copenhagen Street. They were both excited about starting their new life together in their own place. Shortly after making their move, number thirty-five Copenhagen Street came up for grabs. They both decided they could afford the rent as long as they both worked, and so took the plunge. It took them both six months to get the place to their liking. There were prolonged periods of painting, putting up shelves and cleaning. This took up all of their spare time.

There had been no warning. Jennifer's sudden death shocked everyone. Ted had returned from his early shift to find her lying on the sofa they had been given by Jennifer's parents. Ted was now alone. People show grief in many different ways – anger, withdrawal, anxiety, panic or aggression. Along with the numbness and emptiness, Ted experienced feelings of guilt. Why hadn't he been there to help her? Maybe he could have saved her? Why hadn't he noticed anything wrong before going to work that day? Why was it his Jennifer, when there are some awful people in this world?

From day one after her sudden death, Ted felt lonely. He ached with grief. This house was Jennifer's. He could smell her soft skin on the pillow. He touched her clothes in the wardrobe. He stared with a desperate gaze at their wedding photograph on the mantelpiece and the picture of them on their honeymoon in Llandudno. He was lost.

Ted returned to work after the funeral, and typically some of his workmates didn't know how to handle his loss. Some would avoid him or avoid eye contact, then mutter sympathetic words that made them feel uncomfortable. However, work was the best place for him to be. It was a place of normality and the working hours in his day were filled. It was when he came home to an empty house it was hard for him. No beautiful face for him to kiss. No soft arms to hold him.

'Hey! Mister! Any good uns in the sheds?' was a familiar cry from lads as Ted walked to work. These boys were regulars, sitting on a wall that overlooked the main railway line from Preston to the Midlands. Most carried their railway almanac, the Ian Allen train spotter's book.

These kids were obsessed with timetables and engine classes. Engine names and their numbers were assiduously underlined. Taking risks to cop a 'namer' or a 'Jub' often got them into trouble. Some ran across track whilst others shinned over walls and crept into the locomotive sheds. This was all part of their lives as train spotters. In school holidays they camped at the end of a platform or on a bridge just to see and experience steam engines. It was not only good to spot and record trains but to inhale a mixture of smoke, vapourised oil and dioxins, which made the experience complete.

Everyone could easily identify Ted as a railway man. His clothes gave it away. Polished black, steel toe-capped boots, blue dungarees, blue jacket, shirt and tie and a black shiny cap that proudly boasted the British Rail badge. On cold, winter days he wore an old black donkey jacket. His uniform was complete as he carried a white enamel brew can that he would place on a shelf immediately above the firebox door of the engine. A khaki Second World War gas mask case would carry his sandwiches.

'Aye, lads. Watch out for Trinidad and Tobago. Should be along Stott Lane around half eleven!' he shouted back.

'Naa. Got that one loads o' times. Any Winnys?' The boys cried.

'71000, Duke of Gloucester, Brit class is being cleaned for tonight's run to Crewe,' replied Ted. 'But don't let me catch you down the sheds, mind. It's dangerous down there, and it's private property.' Partricroft sheds housed the locomotives that were to be serviced and cleaned. The huge area would also give employment to a cocktail of tradesmen: fitters, boiler smiths, welders, wheel smiths, lathe operators and cleaners, all played their part in keeping rolling stock on the move.

Ted's first inkling that he was being considered as fireman was when he sat and passed the medical and eyesight test. He was delighted when he was told to go to the store room for a bucket of tools and a shovel. It made him really feel the part when he gave the number of his engine to the store man, and then signed for the equipment. He met his first instructor, driver Walter Beesley, a fifty-eight-year-old curmudgeon who'd been driving for years. Walter knew everything about engines, signals, speed restrictions and routes. He could quote the BR rule book in his sleep. The trouble was that Walter didn't seem to like people. Engines instantly obeyed him as he opened the regulator or applied the steam breaks. Ted would experience a hard, no-nonsense learning process whenever he was paired with Walter.

Alongside this practical experience, potential drivers were expected to attend mutual improvement classes, where junior firemen learned the whole range of footplate responsibilities, underlined by the basic premise that both driver and fireman work together as a team, to ensure the safe transportation of passengers or goods.

Ted's first duty as fireman was to fire up the engine. However, there was a Walter way of doing this: make sure when shovelling coal into the firebox you cover all of its surface area with coal. This involved twisting the shovel left and right to achieve maximum combustion. The subtle skill of 'firing' the engine was to avoid making unnecessary smoke and 'blowing off' as it was known. Blowing off reduced the efficiency of the engine and vital steam was lost in this process. Ted learned to observe the colour of the smoke billowing from the engine's chimney. A grey smoke meant the engine was running efficiently, and all parts of the coal were burning. Little and often was Walter's prescription for firing the engine. Coal was to be broken into small lumps about the size of your fist. Six shovels-full and then partly close the firebox doors to create a burning draft.

In those learning years, all aspects of footplate chores were covered. Ted had responsibility for water as well as coal. Water would be taken before a journey from a huge leather pipe and water tank. On long-distance runs the fireman would drop the water scoop that picked up water for the tender, from the water gullies or troughs along the track. Steam pressure gauges and air ventilation valves had to have constant attention.

Ted was determined to master both theory and practice. Jennifer was as enthusiastic as her husband about steam engine codes of practice and protocols. It was, therefore, a poignant moment when Ted was summoned for his final driving test many years after Jennifer had died. He would show the examiners what he could do and he would do it for her. This qualification was for both of them and he knew she would have been extremely proud of him, were he to succeed.

The initial parts of the test that day were done in the office. Ted had to sign the route book that showed his familiarity with the official rail routes. He was tested on signals and the positions of track imperatives and warnings along certain routes. It was after this rigorous theory test that the practical commenced. Ted was given a goods train to drive from Manchester to Liverpool. It was an historic route. It was the route that Stephenson's first passenger service ran.

A foggy, November morning greeted Ted and his fireman on the day of his driver's test. The examiner, Mr Richards, stood on the footplate. Mr Richards wore a long, black woollen overcoat and a black bowler hat. Dressed like this, he looked set for a day at the office rather than several hours on the footplate. Complete with clipboard and pencil, he gave the order for Ted to make steam and depart from Manchester Central Station. Ted immediately responded by checking he had 21 inches of vacuum, then he blew the brake off, wound the engine into gear and then released the steam brake. He followed this by slowly opening the regulator, and a quick pressure check, and the engine eased away gently.

The complication for this journey was fog. Signals were difficult to see, along with the slow down warning signs. Fortunately, on this day the signalmen or plate men had done their job and laid explosive detonators on the track to tell drivers to stop at the signal or slow down. These warnings were invaluable to the driver to ensure a safe passage. Ted would wave to the plate layers as they warmed themselves at braziers outside their signalman's hut. Driving in fog was the ultimate test for any driver and at the end of the journey as Ted's engine pulled into Lime Street Station, Liverpool, Mr Richards complemented Ted on his excellent driving skills. He'd done it! He'd done it for Jennifer. He'd passed. Ted was the youngest driver employed by British Rail. He would keep to the East Lancashire routes for most of his career.

One day, Ted found himself on the Manchester to Blackpool run. It was a warm, bright summer's day as Ted slipped the engine into Talbot Road station, Blackpool. Steam and smoke effused from the locomotive as it slowly came to rest. The smell of this mixture was soon overpowered by the seaside aroma of chips and candy floss. You knew you were then in the fun palace of the North West. The passengers poured out of their carriages onto the platform. Little boys with their buckets and spades, and their mums and dads with suitcases carefully reinforced with an old belt. There was an air of excitement and expectancy on the platform. People were here to enjoy themselves, and so they did. It was common practice for these eager souls to thank the driver and his fireman as they passed the engine and its tender. Both men were busy winding the engine down before preparing it again for its return journey.

It was unfortunate that Ted's fireman thought the platform to be clear of passengers and suddenly blew out a mixture of steam and water, to clear the cylinders through the cylinder cock. The blast showered a family with this concoction. It was a loud and frightening noise. The children, after jumping in the air with alarm, thought it amusing as they received squirts of water on top of their heads. Their mother, however, seemed none too pleased about her drenching. Ted looked onto the platform from the footplate and suddenly realised what had happened. He leapt the four-feet drop down onto the platform to apologise to the lady and her children. She was still shaking. All he had to wipe them down with was an oily rag in his overall pocket.

'I'm terribly sorry madam. I can assure you it was unintentional. You see my fireman thought the platform was empty.' Her children were now laughing at their wet heads and mum had calmed down. Her hat had taken most of the spray.

'Please, if there is any damage to your clothing, let me pay for it?' Ted insisted.

'That won't be necessary. We'll be alright. It's just water, is it?' replied the lady.

'Err, yes. Just water, madam. But I have to report it. Company rules.'

'Can we go onto the engine, mister?' asked her little boy.

'Of course you can. My fireman will show you how it works,' said Ted. 'Here, Tony, show these two the footplate while I take details from their mum!' he continued. A conversation ensued, with Ted continuing to offer profuse apologies.

'Look, I don't want to get you in trouble,' said the lady.

'No, it's company rules, Mrs ... ?' he interjected.

'Dobson, Mrs Dobson.'

By this time the guard had arrived to see what the problem was. He then took down the necessary details of the incident and asked for her address.

'It's, seventeen Nile Street, Pendleton,' she replied.

'I don't believe it! That's four streets down from where I live. I live in Copenhagen Street,' Ted replied excitedly. 'You must know ...' the conversation continued for a good ten minutes whilst her children were amazed by the workings of the engine.

Before long the two of them were smiling and comparing notes. It transpired that she had lost her husband some five years before and since then had struggled to bring up her children.

'Look, I don't want to make a formal complaint about this,' Mrs Dobson said to the guard. 'It was nothing, really.'

'Well, ok,' replied the guard. 'But it has to go in the book.'

At this point, her two youngsters were handed down to her from the footplate and their conversation was forced to cease. The guard then returned along the platform.

It happened completely out of the blue. Ted had no control over his next words. It seemed a reflex response. He surprised himself.

'When you return home from your holidays, would you mind if I called upon you. You, you, you know ...' he stuttered, 'if I could ask you out one evening?'

Mrs Dobson seemed taken aback, but pleasantly so. She smiled and then dropped her head nervously. 'Err, yes ... that would be nice, thank you,' she replied.

Ted then raised his head with pleasure.

'Oh, that's wonderful. Thank you. By the way,' he said, 'I don't know your name?'

'Oh, yes!' she smiled. 'It's Jennifer, Jennifer Dobson.'

As a postscript to this story, Ted and Mrs Dobson courted for two years before he popped the question. In the September of 1966 there was a new Jennifer living at number 35. Out of tragedy blossomed a loving relationship and they remained together for the next forty years.

# The Goodbody Family at Number 21

THE GOODBODY HOUSEHOLD WAS a somewhat recent addition to Copenhagen Street. Gloria Goodbody was mother of twins, Gordon and Davinia. Her husband, Alec, had been newly promoted to supervisor in quality control at Kellogg's in Trafford Park. Gloria was anxious that every member of the Copenhagen Street population knew about his new position.

'Of course, we will be moving very soon. Alec's got a senior manager's job. He's got four hundred people under him. We are looking at properties in Failsworth, not far from Didsbury, you know.' Gloria would broadcast this information to anyone she met. Indeed, it was true about Alec having that number of people under him, but only because he worked on the fourth floor of the factory. Alec was in charge of a work force of ten people whose job was to pick out the burnt cornflakes.

She would also brag to people on the market that they lived in a detached property. She was, in fact, correct. However, number forty-six where they lived was an end of terrace house that was coming away from the rest of the properties because of mining subsidence. She failed to include this structural defect in her conversations. The steps of her home were always freshly donkey-stoned and so too were the window sills. She had trained both Gordon and Davinia to leap over the three spotless steps on their way in or out of the house. For Alec, he had to

69

bring his bicycle around the back entry. She once placed a couple of plant pots, complete with blooms, on the upstairs window ledges. This was to simulate the floral artistry seen on those romantic cottages in the Bastide villages of Provence, she'd seen a picture of such beautiful decoration somewhere in a magazine at the hairdressers. Neighbours took a pessimistic view of such plant husbandry, particularly when on a windy autumnal day one of these decorations blew from its position onto Mrs Thackery below.

'Nearly ruddy killed me that pot plant. I don't know where she thinks she is that woman. This isn't ruddy London ya know. It's Lancashire!' moaned Mrs Thackery, to an audience in the Fusilier's that evening.

Gloria had aspirations of grandeur. She wanted a champagne lifestyle but sadly Alec brought home 'best bitter' money. Gloria was forced to secure employment at a warehouse in Cobden Street. She described the nature of her job as being in property management. To those who worked on those premises she was a cleaner. However, this did not stop her boastful claims to her colleagues.

Declarations such as, 'Tonight we are having Lancashire *calamari a l'oignon*'. This dish when translated to ordinary people speak revealed they were, in fact, having tripe and onions for their tea. This too, led to confusion. Gloria would describe tea as supper and dinner as lunch. Such dining terms baffled her work colleagues. I mean, who would have crumpets for your tea when you'd worked hard all day with nothing in your belly. To ordinary folk, dinner was a hastily gnawed pie, and tea was your main meal such as tater hash. Supper? Well, hard luck, there wasn't any. Remember, in those days, those who professed they fed on tinned peaches and Carnation milk were definitely living above their station.

Should anyone be asked in for a cup of tea then the best china was brought out, and fig and bourbon cream biscuits were exhumed and recycled from a secret tin in the sideboard. Broken Arrowroot biscuits the family normally scoffed were deemed too infra-dig for company. Similarly, when Gloria dispatched Gordon to the chip shop, he would be instructed to purchase hake and a bag of scallops rather than everyone else's cod and chips. However, should the chippy be empty, then it was cod and chips. She would also refer to meat and potato pies as potato and meat pies for some strange reason.

For years Alec would journey to Trafford Park on an old NSU

Quickly motorbike. At Gloria's request he had also purchased a motorbike and sidecar. On Sundays, when the Goodbody clan wished to visit relatives, Gloria would ride pillion and both Gordon and Davinia would be stuffed into the sidecar. Regrettably, Gloria could not fit into the sidecar without great effort. Goodbody by name was not unfortunately coupled with good body in vivo. Someone in the street once described this manoeuvre of her climbing into the sidecar as like watching a morbidly obese snail trying to slip back into its shell. Indeed, Gloria was a capacious lady whose skin folds in a swimsuit would have encouraged anyone to take up origami. She did, however, acknowledge her corpulence and saw it to be an advantage when she joined the Manchester choral society. 'Female opera singers are always stout,' she would say. I think Maria Callas may have disagreed with that pronouncement.

The family would always attend church on Sunday. They were Methodists and never touched a drop of alcohol, except for medicinal reasons. However, when Gloria's arty choral society friends came round, the sherry flowed like the River Irwell and it was hoped God would turn a blind eye – after all, they were soon to put on the Messiah in His honour. Holidays meant the Goodbodys holidaying in Rhyl. Gloria felt that Blackpool was rather vulgar, and there were fewer 'Kiss Me Quick' hats in that Welsh town. They would stay in a caravan for the week, though Gloria insisted on using the term mobile home. Even if their week away was so wet that everyone returned home with 'Trench Foot', Gloria would boast a suntan, courtesy of Kitchen Bouquet gravy browning.

The commendable thing about Gloria was that she wanted the best for her children. She would let them play with only a restricted number of the kids in the street whose pedigree she had already examined. However, Gloria denied Gordon and Davinia access to Grove Street. She viewed all inhabitants of this lawless thoroughfare as riff raff. Gloria would say of the residents of Grove Street, 'It's not the drains you can smell, it's the people.' She once reprimanded a Mr Slocum of number five Grove Street for his son pinching Davinia's bottom on the way to school. His reflex response was to demand that Mrs Goodbody shut her gob and take her posh arse out of the street. The command was peppered with expletives alien to Gloria but she worked out the gist of this message.

Gloria would take her children to the library and encourage them to read; anything from children's adventure books to Dickens. She had ambitions for her progeny. Unfortunately, she could not afford to send them to private school. Instead they had to go to John Street School like everyone else in Copenhagen Street. She was a kind, yet protective mum. The Goodbody kids were the first to read and write in their year. These talents were both due to Gloria's efforts. Alec did what he was told, and participated in model making and taught them how to ride a bicycle. Alec and Gloria were far from sporty. In fact, the closest Alec got to team games was blow football. Gordon never made the school football team, much to his relief. The team sheet always listed him as fifth reserve.

Another one of Gloria's aspirations was for her children to speak with good tone and pronunciation. They experienced little of the Queen's English at John Street School. It was pure Salford-speak there. So, sentences like 'I broke a large bottle of milk by throwing a large stone at it,' would come out as 'I broke vat big bokkle o' milk by chuckin' a dirty big ducker at it.' To prevent Davinia and Gordon from absorbing this contaminated communication, Gloria arranged for Cecilia Laithwaite to give them elocution lessons, once a month. Cecelia was one of Gloria's choral colleagues who spoke very precisely. So, Gordon was schooled in using correct phonetics and would enunciate sentences such as 'In and out and round-about,' as though he was Anthony Eden himself. Davinia, too, would astound her classmates by sounding like Fanny Cradock. Walter Duckinfield, who was an urchin from Gardner Street, and questionably short of a full set of chromosomes, would shout to Gordon and Davinia, 'Are ya' still 'avin' them electrocution lessons, are ya?' This was, indeed, a complex sentence construction for Walter, who normally got by on a mixture of grunts, pointing and flatulence.

Davinia had aspirations higher than her mother, and was a precocious madam. She could be manipulative, demanding and extremely selfish. The few girls with whom she was allowed to play soon became tired of her. She would never turn the skipping rope and always wanted to be first to participate in anything. She would refuse to be 'out' in team games and declined to do things that involved physical exertion. Boys noticed, when she did the occasional handstand, that she wore white frilly knickers as opposed to the navy blue of her female friends.

Davinia did get her comeuppance when an older girl from Hankinson Street with fists as big as baseball gloves, told her exactly what she thought of her and punctuated the critique with a thump on the ear that glowed for days.

It was in June of 1953 that things would change for the Goodbodys. Alec won the work's sweep for the Derby. Gloria suggested that they purchase a television. Black and white television in the United Kingdom was very much in its infancy in those days. Few working class families could afford a television, even paying for it on the drip or renting. Indeed, the statistics for residents who had a television in that year worked out to be one TV for every five streets. Gloria had seen the one she wanted in Arthur Grogan's 'All Things Electric' shop window. It was a GEC, top of the range television. She ignored the cheaper Phillips, nine-inch screen models. The set had a walnut-veneered cabinet with speakers at the side. However, the unique selling point of this machine was that it had a twelve-inch screen. Gloria had admired this set for ages. It had been advertised in the *Daily Mail*. Its advert featured Eamonn Andrews, full of smiles, leaning on its cabinet. At the foot of the newspaper the advert read, 'Brilliant picture, new filter faced long life tube giving full daylight viewing. Yes, the GEC BT5147, 60 guineas, or available on hire purchase.'

A twelve-inch screen was certainly a step closer to royalty for Gloria. Those few members of the proletariat who could rent or pay for a television 'on the knock' had nine-inch screens and were one channel only. Gloria's was capable of receiving three channels, though Associated Rediffusion didn't start broadcasting until September 1955. Nevertheless, three channels were THREE channels to Gloria, and at that time nobody in Copenhagen Street possessed any form of television.

The set was delivered by Arthur Grogan himself, but not before Gloria had announced its coming to most of the street.

'It'll look lovely in the parlour, we've got just the table to stand it on. Walnut on walnut, now that's colour co-ordination.' Gloria had big plans for this television. It would increase her social status in the street. At the start of the sixties, locals would call her the Annie Walker of Copenhagen Street. Her profile amongst the choral society too would rocket. This contraption would make the Goodbodys less working-class and more bourgeois.

Anxious to let the local community know she possessed a television,

Gloria would often leave the parlour window slightly open so that passers-by could catch an earful of 'Quatermass' or even the music supporting the interlude. Gloria's mother was summoned to look at this new device and instantly fell in love with the interlude. 'Oooh, I'd love to be able to make pots like that our Gloria. Can I come round tomorrow at the same time? I'd like to see him make a smaller one with handles this time.' Gloria's dad, Amos, was less than impressed as he sat with a mug of tea staring at the test card. His prediction about television was, 'I can't see what all the fuss is about. It'll never catch on. I'd sooner watch our fire go out. And, there's another thing, our Gloria. How do you know what's happening the other end? I mean, how do we know who's looking at you?' Amos had clearly read George Orwell's *1984* a few years earlier.

One possibility for this television was for Gloria to invite people round to watch particular programmes. In 1955 she invited the Norris family round to watch 'Rin Tin Tin'. As the family was invited into the parlour, each person was charged one penny before being allowed to take their seats that had been placed in front of the screen in a semi-circle. The penny fee did, however, include a cup of tea and an Arrowroot biscuit.

The only thing that went against Gloria's slick production was the fact that the television had to have a time to warm up before any picture became visible. This was due to the instrument being powered by valves that had to have some time for its electrons to feed the cathode ray tube. This hiatus was followed by a picture that seemed to be composed of lots of lines rotating and disappearing back into the screen. On the side of the cabinet were three knobs. The vertical and horizontal hold switches may solve frustrating efforts to change an image of a tall, very thin man, somersaulting back into the screen, into a short, fat man who was relatively stable and not moving up and down.

The pathetic aerial on the top of the walnut cabinet never seemed to be in the right position to receive the signal. Invariably the signal produced a grainy, vibrating image. The dog, Rin Tin Tin, looked rabid as he moved across the screen. To remedy this 405 line malfunction, Gordon was told to stand in the corner of the room and hold the aerial high above his head. The picture now crystallised and Gloria shouted to Gordon, 'That's it love, hold it there!' After about a five-minute spate of aerial holding, Gordon would complain, 'I can't see the picture, mother!'

Gloria would calmly reply, 'That's alright dear, we'll tell you what happens!'

As the group became engrossed in the plot, Gordon complained once more.

'My arm is aching, mum!' This plea for help was firmly dealt with by Mrs Norris. You would sooner chew glass than argue with this lady.

'Shurrup and use yer other arm!' Gordon, therefore, used his other arm.

Such a lucrative enterprise made Gloria think big. She saw an advert in the *Manchester Evening News* for an *accoutrement* for converting your black and white television set to colour. Indeed, I believe it was the descriptor '*accoutrement*' that really impressed her. Gloria had never possessed an *accoutrement* before. Alec was duly sent off to purchase the said accessory from the warehouse off Shude Hill. He returned with a plastic sheet with four suckers, one at each corner, that you pushed against the twelve-inch screen. The plastic cover had many fine lines running through it that dispersed white light. In simple terms it acted as a diffraction grating, throwing out all the colours of the rainbow.

'That bloke's got poor circulation!' shouted Gloria's mother. 'He should never have been allowed to join the police force with lips as blue as that,' she continued.

Gloria's mum was speaking about Jack Warner in an episode of 'Dixon of Dock Green'. She was, in fact, correct about the gentleman. What she failed to notice was that his helmet was green, making him look like an extra-terrestrial. Gloria stuck with the contraption until the comments about pigmentation became rather insulting. Trees glowed red, rivers ran yellow and Muffin the Mule was frighteningly orange.

The money left over from Alec's sweep win saw Gloria purchase a second-hand HMV radiogram. This acquisition really took the Goodbody family into the upper echelons of society. Copenhagen Street would now ring to the tunes of Mantovani, Anne Shelton, Mario Lanza and David Whitfield. Gloria's next door neighbours didn't seem to object to this music. However, during visits from Gloria's choral society, the ordinary citizens of Copenhagen Street did find the loud renderings of 'Carmina Burana' a tad intolerable. As the outspoken Mrs Norris said of this music, 'I see Lady Muck is entertaining her hoity-toity friends again. Ya can't dance or sing along to that twaddle. Beats me what she sees in it!' I am sure Carl Orff, its composer, would have taken on board Mrs Norris's analysis and recorded the karaoke version.

# The Hennessey Family at Number 4

THEY DROPPED MY DAD off in the parlour, two days after he told me he felt a bit queer. We thought something was wrong with him 'cos he didn't bother taking his opening medicine that morning. My dad always took that.

'Guaranteed to get a road through ya!' he would say.

Anyway, Doctor Appleby certified him dead, not long after I'd got back from putting a bet on for my gran. Mind you, that Dr Appleby, I'd never liked him. Always got his nose stuck up in the air. Looked at you as though you're the great unwashed. Before National Health in 1948, gran said she wouldn't have paid him in shirt buttons. My mother hadn't any faith in his medical knowledge, either. She would exclaim, 'Couldn't find his own arse, that bugger!' The other doctor in the partnership had an unpronounceable, Russian-sounding surname. He was far nicer to deal with. He was known to the local community as 'Dr Stopacoff'.

I couldn't make out what it said on the death certificate but it sounded serious with all those long words.

Whenever there's a bereavment in a family it's always the women who know what to do. My mum got her savvy from my gran. She had lost two of her sons, both in the Salford Pals Regiment, killed at Thiepval Ridge, in the Battle of the Somme. You can't get any better training than that.

'I've given 'im a touch o' rouge, Mrs Hennessy. He did look a bit pale and drawn,' said Charles Meredith of Meredith and Sons. Merediths were funeral directors, and had their funeral premises in Union Street. I suppose you'd call it a funeral parlour. It had a shop window, behind which was a marble tombstone carrying the inscription RIP. Around it were various cemetery artefacts such as stone flower vases, concrete grave edging and green marble chippings.

At the back of the display was a wall of purple velvet curtains complete with moth holes. A couple of stands carried photographs of grand and ostentatious graves boasting cherubic figures carved into a huge stone cross. Such funereal finery was reserved for the 'haves' of the city, the aldermen, mill owners and chief constables. Then there was a locality known as the 'have nots'. The area where we lived, pushed to one side of the city, was for the demographic group referred to as 'the have absolutely bugger alls', as my Uncle Cyril would frequently inform people.

Across the top of their window was inscribed 'bespoke undertakers' in bold, silver script. On a small noticeboard by the shop door a poster advertised the 'pay before you go' scheme. The full works for seven pounds seventeen shillings and sixpence. These were funerals 'on the drip'. It proposed buy now, die later. Once more, my pragmatic yet poetic Uncle Cyril referred to it as death on tick.

Mr Meredith and his young, pimply assistant removed the coffin lid. Mr Meredith wore a long black coat with black buttons that reminded me of Pontefract cakes. Meredith pointed out to my mother that over the years, we'd only paid in seven pounds.

'I'm sure we can come to some arrangement, Mrs Hennessey. You could have cheaper handles, or leave off the inscribed brass name plate. I'd choose that if I were you. After all, you know who he is and I am sure he does,' pointing to the deceased. We went for the latter.

'There, what d' ya think?' he confidently enquired, as he drew me and my mother alongside the coffin,

'I put clean underpants on 'im as you'd said. The satin lining inside the box brings up his suit really well, doesn't it?' he continued.

'Oh!' said my mother, looking rather surprised by her husband's new-found rosy cheeks. 'He does look a bit, err ... pink.'

'I wanted him to look fresh, and natural. Aye, fresh and natural Mrs Hennessy. You know there are some undertakers who don't pay attention to fine detail. Take the Co-op, for instance. They make everyone look as though they've just come back from a week's heat wave in Rhyl. That's not us, Mrs Hennessey, fresh and natural,' he concluded. 'If you'd have let me put his teeth in I could have made him look as if he were smilin', he added as an afterthought.

'No, he was quite clear about that, he wanted to leave 'em to Walter Pridmore, his dominoes partner. He'd barely had six months use out of 'em. They'll go to a good home,' mother replied.

'Fair enough, Mrs Hennessey. You're the customer. We'll be here eleven sharp on Thursday. Just the one car wasn't it?' he confirmed, as he propped the coffin lid in the corner of the room.

It was customary to 'lay out' corpses in your front room in those days. The parlour was only used on special occasions. Ours had the compulsory aspidistra by the front window. It stood on a long wooden pedestal in a pot. I suppose posh folk today would call it a jardinière and pay a fortune for it. We got ours from Loony Len on Salford market for one shilling and four pence, and he chucked in the aspidistra as well.

I always found this a dull room, with its brown floral wallpaper, absorbing what sunlight there was. It was even darker now because mourning etiquette at that time forced my mother to close the curtains. Such a practice told passers-by there had been a death in the family, and was also designed to prevent nosy folk from looking in. Again, our sagacious Uncle Cyril pointed out that such practice was also wise because it stopped any hot sun making him 'go off' quicker. Cyril, ever the practical man, could be an asset to any conversation, particularly at times of family grief.

To the left-hand side of the room sat the horse-hair sofa. I always objected to the monthly visits from my Uncle Derek and Auntie Hilda for two reasons. First was the fact they would arrive on a motorbike and then refuse to take off their leathers and crash helmets as they sipped tea and dunked 'Nice' biscuits. Hilda would head butt me with her helmet as she bent forward to give me the customary family kiss.

'Oops! Sorry love. I'm keepin' it on, chuck. It helps keep me perm in.' This was her excuse for the facial trauma I had just received. The second objection to this reunion was that I would be forced to sit on that sofa for a couple of hours. I slowly developed a rash from its contact with the skin on the back of my legs. Mum always had to rub in a bit of calamine after they'd gone.

On the wall opposite was the fireplace with its black, cast iron surround. There was a row of floral tiles flanking the fire grate, two of which bore a diagonal crack. Only in the winter would this fire be lit when we had 'company'. As soon as they'd gone it was back to sub-zero once more, and the ice would form on the inside of the front window. Consequently, there was always the ritual of airing the room before this 'company' arrived.

The mantelpiece had a clock, surrounded by a dark wood frame. The clock always said a quarter to nine. My dad had lost its key some years ago. Indeed, time had stood still in that room. Nothing changed. Next to this worthless timepiece was a faded picture of mum and dad on their wedding day. From the look on their faces, I don't know why they bothered. Their looks confirmed that marriage is, indeed, a serious business and not to be photographed. My mum, though, had a pretty face, enhanced by the white laced veil that lay across her head, secured in place by a couple of flowers. Dad looked as though he was troubled with engorged haemorrhoids, even at that young age. That same suit of his still hung on the back of their bedroom door.

'You never know when it'll come in handy,' were his reasoned words.

An oval mirror hung from its chain above the clock. Its edges were blistered and had lost their reflective powers. Uncle Cyril reckoned these were caused by Auntie Hilda's visits. She would look into it when she arrived and then stare at it once more before they departed. Cyril would say of Hilda, 'She's got a face that would frighten a police horse, that woman!'

Flanking the fireplace on both sides were two armchairs. My dad claimed they were Chesterfields. Cyril would quip, 'Found in a field, in Chesterfield more like!' If you sat down quickly on them they would puff out a miasma of dust. It took a good thirty seconds for the corpulent Auntie Hilda to become visible after she had taken her seat.

The carpet was wafer thin and a mixture of red and black. It finished a good twelve inches short of the skirting boards. Filling the space between it and the wall was dark green lino that would rise from the floor in places and curl up at the edges. My mother forced dad to bash down the lino with carpet tacks following another visit from the motorbike duo. She was carrying the tea on a tray but tripped over the protruding lino by the door. Derek and his spouse caught the lot but remained scald free and dry thanks to their leathers and crash helmets.

This underused room, resembling an LMS railway station waiting room, now doubled as a funeral parlour where friends, neighbours and relatives could enter to pay their last respects to the deceased. The elderly seemed to love a good funeral. It was for them a social occasion, and also a time when families in the same street were far more together and mutually supportive than they are today.

'Is he in there, love?' probed Mrs Mavis Boyson, pointing to the front room as she was welcomed by my mother.

'I've come with Mr Pridmore. Sorry, I've got the two grandchildren in tow. I'll not be a minute,' she added.

Mavis worked behind the counter in the post office. She was known as a jovial soul who would offer a free lick with every stamp bought. Such benevolence would frequently get her into trouble at Christmas when she honoured her pledge, but by the end of a December morning her lips seemed welded together with gum. She did, however, have a sense of humour and when one of her customers began flirting with her and then asked for ten stamps, adding 'And one for yerself ya gorgeous creature,' Mavis thought him a real wag. The rest of her customers waiting patiently in the queue did not.

My mum opened the parlour door for Mrs Boyson, the two kids and Walter Pridmore. Mavis quickly advanced towards the coffin and peered down at my dad.

'Oh, Lotty love, doesn't he look well?' she exclaimed. 'Is that his Sunday best? The one he wears for the Legion?' she continued. At this point, one of the scruffy urchins grabbed hold of one of the coffin handles and started to bang it against the side of the coffin like a doorknocker. The action went unnoticed by the two women, who seemed preoccupied my with dad's appearance.

'Do ya not think he looks a bit pink, Mavis?' inquired my mum, continuing to show concern over her husband's new-found glow.

'Oh, no Lotty, it's taken years off him. Who's buryin' 'im?'

'Merediths,' answered my mum.

'Ooooh! I thought you might have gone for the Co-op, what with the divvy an' all,' she replied.

Mavis carefully observed the corpse from head to toe with all the scrutiny of a pathologist. The kid continued to hammer the coffin handle against the wooden box and the younger one started to pull back the curtains.

'Hey, pack it in Lawrence and you, Leonard. Gerr off them curtains! Show some respect if you please?' shouted Mrs Boyson whilst simultaneously giving both of them a slap.

'They've done a lovely job, haven't they Mr Pridmore?' she said as she then turned to address this tall, thin man.

'Yes, he looks peaceful, Mrs Hennessey, almost as though he's sleeping. Errr ... did he happen to mention anything about his teeth, Mrs Hennessey?' he inquired.

'I've got 'em in a glass in t'scullery, Mr Pridmore. He were most insistent you have 'em before he went. I'll go and put 'em in a rag for ya,' replied my mother as she turned to exit the room.

'Did he mention anything about his dominoes, Mrs Hennessey? Ya know, the ivory set he used at the Fusilier's for special matches?' he added.

'No, he didn't. I were thinkin' of puttin' them with him in his coffin along with a bottle of pale ale,' mother replied. 'He loved his pale ale.'

'Oh, err ... just askin', Mrs Hennessey. Those dots have seen a lot of action. Pity to let them go to waste.'

'Well, let's hope he can give Saint Peter a game when he's up there. No, Mr Pridmore, they're going in the coffin. I'll go and get yer teeth.'

Mrs Boyson then delivered both kids yet another slap as they played with the coffin lid in the corner.

Mr Pridmore's disappointment at such news was clear. He quietly said to Mrs Boyson, 'A waste, Mavis. A waste. He does look good though, doesn't he? Best I've ever seen him look. In the pink I would say.'

'I don't think Mrs Hennessey would like you to use that term Mr Pridmore,' Mavis sharply replied.

Thursday arrived. We'd been up since six buttering barm cakes and slicing boiled ham for the wake. A table had been laid in the living room. There were some slices of Madeira cake and a few sausage rolls. Ossie Tattersall, the local butcher, supplied the ham and had thrown in some haslet and tongue for people with more discerning tastes. Uncle Cyril took charge of libation. Bottles of Mackeson for the old ladies and Threlfalls pale ale for everyone else. There was, however, the customary bottle of VP sherry, exhumed from the Christmas festivities. Auntie Hilda would shift most of that.

'They're here, Lotty. The car's just pullin' up outside o' th' house,' called Cyril. My mother was finishing off chores in the scullery.

'Do ya want to see him once more before they put t'lid on? He does look peaceful,' she shouted.

'He looks quite dead to me,' Cyril muttered to himself. 'Err, no thanks, Lotty. I'd sooner remember him as he was,' he shouted.

'Do the flowers look alright, I ordered them from Meredith's as part of the package?' she inquired.

'Lovely, Lotty. Lovely. I notice they spell Fred and not Frederick though?' he queried.

'It would have been half a crown more for that,' she answered.

'Penny pinchin' buggers, them Merediths. Meredith senior ought to try washin' an' all. Folk reckon he hides his money under the soap!' quipped Cyril, our family philosopher.

There was me, mum, granddad, gran and Cyril in the car. Derek and Hilda followed on their motorbike. The rest of the aunts and uncles, friends and workmates met us at the church and then, after the service, went on to the cemetery.

Father Dolan conducted the service even though dad and him never got on. 'Next time he comes knockin' on my front door tellin' me I haven't been to church for months, I'll put one on 'im. Do ya hear me Lotty? I only got married in the Catholic church 'cos you were a left footer. And, as for tryin' to convert me, I nearly choked him with his rosary beads. He can bugger off!' my dad would proclaim.

The eulogy was given by Father Dolan with a few words from Uncle Derek. Father Dolan spoke of people who did not understand the rewards of going to heaven. He talked about 'those who were afraid of dying, and their lack of faith meant going to a dark and horrible place'. I overheard Uncle Cyril quietly whisper to Mrs Anderton's fancy man, 'Is he talkin' about Prestatyn?'

Derek showed respect and had removed his crash helmet.

My mother burst out crying when Derek reminded us all of dad's penchant for trying to be the life and soul of our Christmas parties. My dad would predictably say to Hilda each Christmas Day, 'Can I press you to a jelly, Hilda?'

Hilda would roar with laughter. The volume of her response was in direct proportion to the number of glasses of sherry she had consumed. Derek also reminded us of my dad's other yuletide habit of putting my mother's scarf on his head and leading us in his repertoire of Vera Lynn songs. Totally embarrassing for me but the rest of the family and friends thought him to be both troubadour and comedian.

The Meredith team led us from the church to the graveside. It must have been an uncomfortable journey for my dad because one of the pallbearers appeared to have some sort of nervous tic. To prevent it from falling from their shoulders, his colleagues suddenly made a grab for the coffin each time he twitched. I also noticed that this final part of the funeral process appeared to be rather hurried. I frequently saw Mr Meredith senior look at his watch. Confirming my suspicion of their apparent haste, the four assistants lowered the coffin into the grave with all the precision and care of making a boulder crash from the top of a cliff.

There was a distinctly audible 'splosh' as the casket finally came to rest. It landed with such force that it sent a wave of water up in the air, soaking the assembled mourners. To justify and explain everyone's new found hydration, Mr Meredith senior whispered to my mum, as he wiped the muddy water from her black overcoat with his grubby hanky, 'We've had a lot of rain recently, Mrs Hennessy.' As everyone took a small handful of earth and dropped it onto the coffin we saw the wooden box floating in the water, as buoyant as a ketch in an offshore breeze.

I observed the hearse leave the cemetery with the acceleration of a formula one racing car at Silverstone. We too were ferried back to our house by a Merediths protégé at breakneck speed, my gran nearly parting company with her hat as we shot round Viaduct Street.

'Here! What's all the rush?' shouted my granddad.

'We've got a one o'clock in Lower Broughton,' the employee replied.

'Listen son,' said granddad, 'dead people won't go without you. So, slow down!'

The curious thing about a wake is the fact that people you've never seen before turn up. There were two at my dad's who nobody knew, yet they claimed they used to work with him years before. They both stood in the corner, each downing pale ale and demolishing most of the sausage rolls. 'I don't know,' I heard one say to the other, 'I've been to so many funerals recently, my suit's starting to smell of boiled ham.'

I was told to mingle, and make sure everyone had a drink. There was no need to check on Auntie Hilda. She was perched next to the sherry, her glass always half full. She had made an effort today though. She wore a tight black skirt and an equally tight blouse. Hilda was not short in the bosom area, as every male at this gathering seemed to observe.

'Aye, she shoves it all in the top window, does our Hilda.' My granddad would say. There was no crash helmet, yet she insisted on draping her fox fur stole over her leather jacket. This fur drape was a constant source of amusement to kids because the eyes in its head looked crossed, giving the animal a spaced-out look.

Mr and Mrs Jackson were friends of our family. Mum had worked with Betty at Epstein's rainwear factory. Betty was what I would call a professional mourner and took her role seriously. She proclaimed, 'I always look in the deaths column in the *Reporter* every week. Well, Lotty, we're at that age, you see. Do you remember Elsie Cardwell? Oooh, you must remember her. Dark-haired woman, lived at the top of Cromwell Street. Five children, had 'em very quick … cancer.' This final word forced you to lip read since it was never spoken. It was a word that predicted doom, and a word with which everyone seemed uncomfortable. This fear continues today.

'Have you thought of what words should go on the tombstone, Lotty? You know, a cenotaph or whatever they call it?' she continued.

'Well, yes we have, Betty. I want the words, "Gone But Not Forgotten,"' mother shouted, full of emotion.

'Who's that, Lotty?' enquired Auntie Hilda from across the room.

I blame it on the sherry.

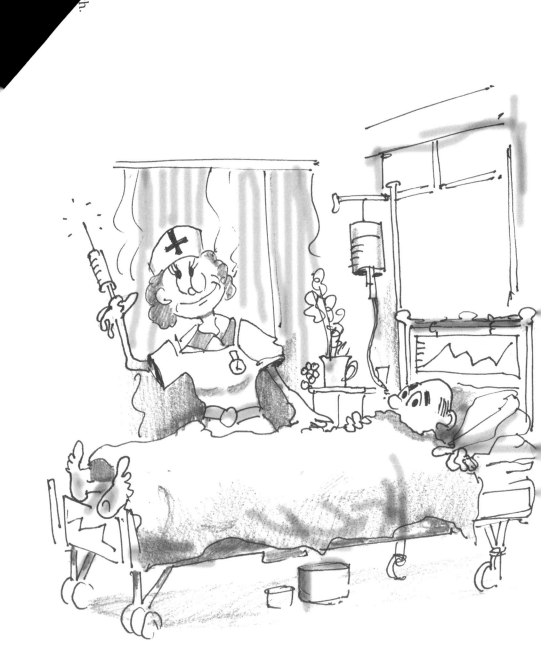

# The Acheson Family at Number 14

'Y OU'LL END UP A spinster, our Shirley, I'll tell ya that for nowt. An old maid. That's what they'll call ya if ya go into that job!' bawled Mr Cedric Acheson, father of three girls, of whom Shirley was the youngest.

'Why don't ya do something with regular hours an' all, like our Mary and Julie?' he continued.

'Oh, leave her alone father, it's a vocation and you should be proud of her,' replied Vera, his wife.

'Well, I've never heard of any job like it. You have to leave if you want to get married? Is she becomin' a nun? It's nonsense. Nonsense, I tell ya ... and another thing, why can't she live here, at home? We could do with the money. Why has she got to live in at that place?' complained Cedric.

'It's what they all have to do in nursing when they start training. I thought you might be pleased for her, having passed her school certificates. She's a good kid, Cedric. Let her be. Anyroad, it'll be one less for you to moan at when you find the toilet seat down,' she concluded.

Shirley Acheson was one of twenty ladies who enrolled on the State Registered Nurse course in September 1949. She was to start her three-year apprenticeship at Hope Hospital and reside in the nurses' home on the same site. Nursing was seen as a vocation. It had to be a true calling because many viewed the hours, salary, conditions of service and the nature of the work to be unattractive. A starting salary of £4 per week rising to £9 upon qualification, underlined its lack of appeal.

Uniform was standard issue, with a white cap and long white bib protecting the pale blue dress underneath. Black laced shoes and black stockings completed the outfit. Short sleeves with elasticated frilly cuffs replaced the long sleeves of the 1940s. The caps had to be folded in a special way and were eventually replaced by paper ones. Everything in the uniform was starched and made crumpling noises as the women bent forward. The trick was not to get the pinny dirty before matron's rounds. They were also issued with a navy blue cloak with a bright red lining. The cape was warm and came in very handy particularly when on nights. Jewellery was not allowed and makeup was to be at a minimum. To complete the attempt at removing your civvy street identity, they were known to everyone by their surname, which was very formal and business-like. It tended to lack friendliness and orders were fired from the ward sister to her workforce like bullets from a machine gun.

After a short period in the nursing training school, learning anatomy, physiology and hygiene, Shirley found herself on a medical ward looking after patients with illnesses such as chronic chest problems, heart disease, kidney failure and even alcohol abuse. The city had an extremely high number of chronic bronchitis cases because of a multitude of factors, including climate, pollution, poor nutrition and smoking. Many elderly citizens finished up in these wards. Some patients would be discharged after a couple of weeks of drug therapy and care. Indeed, it was the norm in those days for patients to spend weeks rather than days in hospital. A hernia repair would see you incarcerated for a week as opposed to today's day care surgery, being admitted at 7 a.m. and discharged at 4 p.m. the same day. Certain aged patients were deemed too far gone for treatment on this ward, and would end their days on a geriatric unit.

Much attention was given to the daily hygiene of the building. Floors had to be scrubbed and then buffed. Before Matron's rounds, beds were pulled out then pushed back. The floor of the ward resembled the quarter-deck of HMS Ark Royal, only here student nurses busied themselves with mop and bucket rather than Jolly Jack Tar. Patients' lockers were cleaned, the sluice room had to sparkle, and there was no such thing as a dirty window in the ward. Nurses too were not exempt from a scrub and a polish. Junior nurses were instructed to scrub up to their elbows between each service given to patients.

Most wards housed forty beds. Patients at the top of the ward, near sister's office and the nursing station, were the poor souls deemed extremely unwell and needing close monitoring. The Grim Reaper often patrolled these beds. Should you be in bed at the bottom of this long room then you knew things weren't so serious and your discharge was imminent.

Patients who could sit out of bed were not supposed to make the place untidy and were unceremoniously forced back in bed on matron's rounds and when doctors chose to visit. Junior doctors daren't upset the sister. Should they ever antagonise her then they would have to make their own tea or fetch their own patients' case notes.

Matron was regarded by all as the hospital supremo. She was in charge of absolutely everything. Patient care, catering, laundry, cleaning, recruitment and retention of staff, nurse training and accommodation, all featured on her job sheet. Shirley had met Matron Balding at her interview and quickly realised you did not upset her. She was a portly woman and a typical mesomorph who attempted a figure of eight body shape through the use of a tight white belt with its polished silver, sculptured buckle in the centre. This structure appeared to act like a truss, holding apart the upper and lower halves of her body.

Shirley's new lodgings for the next year was to be the nurses' home, on site at the hospital. Matron saw to it that this residence was to be used for sleeping and study. There were very strict rules about socialising. Men were not allowed in the female section and vice versa. Indeed, if any male form was found inside this building, the offender was classified fit for prosecution by the police and the poor girl he was intending to meet lost her job. Shirley and her fellow student nurses felt they were under close scrutiny. Matron would inspect their rooms and rummage through their drawers and also their drawers. The cleaners were regarded as those who would snitch on you and report you to matron.

One of the first skills Shirley had to learn was how to make a bed. It was not just any old bed but a hospital bed. This item of furniture, complete with its rubber-lined mattress, had to be dressed in a special way.

'First the foot, and then the head. That's the way to make a bed.' This feeble attempt at poetry was drummed into the nursing rookies in the first week of nursing school. Bottom sheets were carefully folded at each corner, and this was followed by laying a small rubber sheet half way along the bed, and then covering it with a starched drawsheet. This must have made lying in bed a most uncomfortable experience, particularly for the anatomy around your bottom. A top sheet, blanket and counterpane followed, all folded and tucked away with hospital precision.

Should a patient develop bed sores then this was viewed as poor nursing. Patients whose bed rest was for a long period had to be turned at hourly intervals like a chicken on a spit roast. Hips, ankles, shoulders and bottoms were rubbed with surgical spirit in the hope that the skin would toughen and resist the friction caused between body mass and starched sheets.

The youthful Shirley was full of enthusiasm and eager to learn. She had been taught that the patients were her customers and that their welfare was paramount. Because of Shirley's willingness to please in those early days she did make some mistakes. However, she quickly learned from them and never repeated these errors.

Her first nursing blunder involved a patient with chronic breathing problems. The gentleman was complaining to her that he hadn't had a good night's sleep for ages.

'Well, it's quiet on the ward now, Mister Longhurst. Why don't you try forty winks,' she suggested. To help the sleep-deprived chap 'drop off', she took four of his pillows away and lay him flat on the bed and bade him goodnight. It was fortunate for Mr Longhurst, and unfortunate for Shirley, that the ward sister quickly spied him supine.

'What the hell's going on here Acheson? Are you trying to kill your patient?' shouted sister. During his brief horizontal experience, Mr Longhurst had turned blue and was gasping for air.

'This man should be upright in bed all of the time so that he can breathe more easily, you stupid girl. That's what those five pillows are for. You've only been on my ward five minutes and you nearly caused a fatality. See me in my office Acheson, now!'

Unfortunately, one *faux pas* was swiftly followed by another. She was asked to help give out the medicines from the mobile medicine trolley under the supervision of staff nurse Thomas. A crisis occurred when a patient appeared to choke on a boiled sweet. Staff nurse Thomas quickly leapt to his assistance with a Heimlich manoeuvre. The offending confection shot across the ward and landed on the bed of Mr Ringwood, who was a slightly confused pensioner at the best of times. The said gentleman picked up the sweet missile from his bed counterpane and proceeded to suck it and see. During the commotion Shirley mistakenly gave Mr Ringwood a laxative meant for Mr Parsons. Mr Ringwood, unlike Mr Parsons, was regular as clockwork. Serves him right for being greedy, some would say. Others, such as Sister Balding, did not see it this way, and gave both staff nurse and Shirley an almighty roasting which lasted almost half an hour. Once more, Shirley had avoided her first glimpse of a P45.

Student nurses were taught to give doctors the greatest of respect. Junior nurses were in awe of their knowledge and capability. They were expected to open doors for them, offer them a chair, and make them tea. They were to be responsible for completing a patient's chart, measuring pulse and breathing rates, as well as more unpleasant duties such as monitoring and recording urine output. More senior and experienced nurses such as ward sisters or charge nurses were found to have less respect for junior medical staff, probably because they knew more about a patient's condition than the young doctors.

Shirley overheard Sister Braithwaite overrule a junior doctor prescribing 200 mg of penicillin for a wheezing seventy-year-old.

'Could you write that in the patient's notes, Doctor Walsh? 500 mg of penicillin. Nurse, could you draw up the 500 mg of penicillin? It was 500 mg you said, Doctor Walsh, wasn't it?'

The embarrassed young medic, realising his initial prescriptive blunder, visibly reddened and then plucking up a confident deep voice, replied, 'Yes, of course sister. 500 mg, if you please, nurse.'

The antibiotic penicillin, and its subsequent derivatives, were the first of the powerful and effective group of antibacterial agents. Streptomycin was next hailed as a wonder drug in targeting tuberculosis. At nursing school, Shirley and her fellow trainees were given instruction on how to administer penicillin. It was given as an intramuscular injection into the patient's bottom. This procedure had to be done precisely into the upper, outer quadrant of the cheeks of the patient's rear. Anywhere else could result in paralysing the leg. Such news terrified these new recruits and would, no doubt, have alarmed their patients too.

'Can't we draw a cross on the patient so we know where to jab?' enquired Lilly Bradwell. 'I'm no good at darts.'

Shirley decided to gain more confidence with these injections by practising on oranges. She now viewed everyone's buttocks as a pair of Sevilles and refused to eat an orange from that day on.

In the early 1950s there were no plastic syringes or IV bags. Instead glass was used. There wasn't the disposable or throw-away culture that exists today. Most items were reusable and had to be sterilised. Each ward had its steriliser that boiled kidney dishes, syringes, needles and IV catheters. Needles were often sharpened but still hurt as they penetrated your skin. Diabetics had skin as tough as leather but were forced to persevere with needles that made you feel you were injecting yourself with a blunt spear.

Another early calamity saw Shirley dropping three glass syringes that were too hot to handle as she removed them from the autoclave. Two smashed as they hit the floor. The sound of breaking glass brought Sister Maddox into the room.

'You'll have to pay for those breakages, Acheson!' she shouted. Indeed the cost of their replacements came out of her next pay packet.

The sluice room contained two pieces of apparatus for cleaning bed pans and urine bottles. These sanitary items were made of stainless steel and could be washed under pressure in these devices. They emerged hot and gleaming, ready for the next patient. At training school they stressed the importance of allowing them to cool before some poor unsuspecting soul decided to sit on one of them. Sanichairs were an alternative and were commodes on wheels. Shirley's ward had one with a dodgy wheel and always took you off at right angles to where you really wanted to go. Mr Gillespie, a curmudgeon of a man, would cry out to Shirley as she attempted to push him back to his bed, 'That's not my bed! Why are you taking me over here? I finished up in the bathroom last week. Have you no sense of direction, nurse?'

It was imperative that the start of a morning shift saw charts completed. Forty pulses were followed by forty respirations and then forty temperatures.

Thermometers were mercury in glass. Before taking someone's temperature, the mercury line had to be physically forced down behind the constriction line by violently shaking it. Shirley quickly learned never to shake the thermometer if her hands were wet otherwise the thermometer could finish up the other side of the ward. Thermometers were dipped in a pink disinfectant before placing under a patient's tongue. The exception being Mr Ringwood, whose cerebral confusion meant that placing the thermometer under his armpit was safer than in his mouth because he had an uncanny tendency to crunch things from boiled sweets to glass thermometers. However, on days when Mr Ringwood decided to cause the nursing staff problems, student nurse Bradwell said she felt like inserting this thermometer somewhere else!

Shirley's training led her to working on surgical wards, gaining experience of how to dress wounds and remove stitches. Her six-week spell on casualty gave her plenty of practice at closing wounds with these sutures. Her talents grew to include setting up IV drips and post-operatively manage any surgical procedures, from a straight forward appendicitis to a colostomy. Again, it was glass IV bottles, not today's light weight plastic IV kits, that were held high on metal stands. The aseptic technique was stressed in nursing school and cross infection was kept to a minimum but there were no sanitising solutions for medical staff or visitors to use. Doctors wore white coats and used stethoscopes with orange rubber tubing. Blood pressures were taken using mercury in glass contraptions. Taking a patient's blood pressure was deemed a skill reserved for doctors. However, this was soon to change.

Perhaps one of the most upsetting times for Shirley was working on the infectious disease ward. Smallpox scares around that time made her mother fear for her safety. Scarlet fever and diphtheria took no pity on young children. The fifties was not a good decade for infectious disease management and control. In 1952 there were 3,000 deaths from polio and 34,000 from tuberculosis. The 1957 influenza epidemic saw 62,000 fatalities. Places called sanatoriums or isolation hospitals dealt with these sinister infectious diseases and many were annexes to the main general hospital or buildings located away from the city in the countryside.

The frightening breathing contraption referred to as the iron lung gave polio patients help with their respiratory movements.

Other apparatus such as rocking beds gave similar temporary relief. Tuberculosis was treated with antibiotics, improved diet and fresh air, and plenty of it. Patients would be wheeled out onto a veranda outside the main ward, blanketed up, and left there until lunchtime. Patients in the acute stage of this disease were barrier nursed and Shirley had to wear a disposable mask, gown and footwear when she visited the isolation rooms of these poor souls.

The children's ward saw Shirley serve up post-surgical bowls of ice cream and jelly to paediatric tonsil and adenoid victims. Prior to the barbaric surgery the children would be wrapped in a blanket and laid on a rug in front of a roaring coal fire complete with fire guard. Her job was to comfort them and respond to their cries of 'I want me mummy! I want me mum!' She was also to run after the more determined and nimble homesick tots who decided to leg it before facing the surgeon's knife. The tonsillectomies were performed with rapidity and the journey from fireside back to hospital bed via theatre was as slick as a Tesco checkout.

Understaffing was a constant problem on wards. Surgical and gynaecology wards were particularly busy. They had to deal with new, acute admissions as well as sort out the daily minutiae of dressing wounds and looking after patients both pre- and post-surgery. On occasions, beds were placed in the middle of the ward as they were forced to take on new admissions Shirley would describe aspects of nursing as learning a new language. Surgical instruments such as retractors, Cheatle's and Spencer Wells forceps, were easily recognised by all nurses. Surgical procedures such as laparotomy and subtotal gastrectomy were as familiar to them as Al Martino and Frankie Lane.

On her days off, Shirley went home to visit her parents and sisters. She was no sooner up the front doorsteps than her mother gave her a list of people she should go round to visit.

'Mum, I'm not a doctor!' she would say. 'Mrs Kirkwood should take him to the doctor's surgery if she thinks Alfie has got croup,' she continued.

'Well, I know that our Shirley, but she did lend us that cup of sugar when we ran out last Sunday,' replied Mrs Acheson. 'Oooh and while you are round there, I said you'd drop in to old Mr Modley and look at his chest. He thinks he's got a rash from them Thermogene pads he puts on. Poor bloke, he can hardly catch his breath sometimes.'

'Mum, it's me day off. I've had enough of sick people. I just want to go to the pictures with our Julie,' Shirley moaned.

'But people look up to you now you're a nurse, our Shirley. They think you know things,' persisted her mum. 'Go on love, do that for me will ya? There's a good girl.'

'Oh, alright mam but I don't want to get into a habit of doing this.'

'I know love and there's no reason you should ... ya couldn't pop in to see granddad Acheson as well love, could ya? He says his feet are playin' him up again.'

As a postscript to this story, Shirley qualified as SRN after three years training at Hope, Salford Royal, Crumpsall and Ladywell hospitals. Shirley met a nice young man, as her mother called him, and they were married at the end of Shirley's next eighteen months training. This took place at Prestwich hospital where she received the RMN qualification for psychiatric nursing. Shirley then returned to Salford Royal hospital where she became a ward sister before leaving the job to have children. She eventually returned to nursing part time when the children were older.

# The Turnbull Family
# at Number 7

YOU COULD SET YOUR watch by them. Ten o'clock every weekday morning they would sit downstairs in the café huddled around a wooden table, and each with a mug of tea. The average age of this quartet was deceased. Someone once said of them, 'If that lot had ever visited Egypt, then Tutankhamun would have popped out to visit them!' These four ladies would occupy this space for two hours in the warm, and sip their tea until Elsie Turnbull, manageress of the UCP café and shop, would ask them to leave.

'Right ladies, if you wouldn't mind, we've got to get ready for the dinner-time rush. Any longer on them seats and yer'll catch bedsores!'

Conditioned by this daily request, they would all slowly rise and vacate the shop, telling each other they would meet up the next day.

'Same time, same place, Ethel,' called Jessie Maidment as she left the premises. Jessie was the most senior of this cabal of pensioners. She found it difficult to walk upright, and she could be seen on the market practically bent double to such a degree that people felt sure her handbag was on casters. Her grandson, Eric, would always ask of his mum, 'Do I have to kiss grandma? She's got whiskers and it hurts!' It certainly was painful because one of her moles had four sharp hairs protruding from its core that could easily have doubled as hypodermic needles. Nevertheless, she was the mother superior of this group of time-worn tea swiggers, and answered to no one except Elsie Turnbull. Elsie tolerated this ageing group even though their daily bill never exceeded two shillings. She jested to Marion, the assistant manager, that she had given her husband permission to put a pillow over her face if she reached their age. Elsie also moaned about the café smelling of Ralgex for a good hour after they'd gone.

Elsie and her husband Jack lived at number seven Copenhagen Street. Jack had retired early from Metro Vickers due to an industrial accident a couple of years earlier. The principal breadwinner was thus Elsie, who had run the UCP shop and its café for the past fifteen years. The acronym UCP stood for United Cattle Products and in simple terms meant purveyors of offal and included all parts of the cow apart from its lean meat or flesh. Some witty soul referred to a UCP shop as 'The Innard Sanctum'. The building was one of two tripe shops on Broad Street, one sold the cold produce to be taken home whilst Elsie's emporium was much bigger and housed a café and also a shop. Tripe shops sold all kinds of offal and viscera. The fifties continued to be an age of frugality and make-do and mend. These cuts were taken from the most unexpected and obscure parts of the animal, and were known as cheap and nutritious foods. Thus, the cold marble shop frontage exhibited strange anatomical items such as jellied pigs' trotters, chitterlings, tongue and sweat breads. If you put this terminology under the microscope, you would discover you were, in fact, viewing pigs' feet, intestine, an ox's tongue and the thymus gland of a pig. All of these delicacies sold well along with other delights such as brawn, haslet, elder, rissoles, cow-heel, liver, kidneys and black puddings. The best seller that was cheap and heavily consumed was, of course, tripe.

UCP emporia were known as tripe shops and tripe was their unique selling point. Tripe? Well, it's like Marmite. You either like or loathe it. In 1955 there were 146 UCP premises in the North West. Tripe was fundamentally the first three sections of a cow's stomach and manifested itself as smooth or blanket tripe, honeycomb and thick seam. There also existed black tripe that was regarded as a cut above the rest and was, in fact, sheep's stomach. All of its forms were cleaned and bleached in starch at tripe-dressing factories and were delivered in large wooden tripe boxes. Holes in the sides of the boxes allowed the excess starch suspension to leak out. Tripe dressing, as it was called was a skilled occupation. It was also a stinky job and any tripe dressers on their way home from work would be guaranteed the top deck of the bus to themselves.

These gastric morsels were usually eaten raw with salt, vinegar and pepper. A slice of tomato would give the dish an extra piquancy as it slipped down your throat. Honeycomb tripe was popular with kids because they loved filling its cells with vinegar. Apparently some optimistic entrepreneur thought dried honeycomb tripe would make excellent carpet underlay. He opened his business in July 1957 and sadly went bankrupt in September of that year. Thick seam was not for the faint-hearted because it had a huge fatty rib running through its body. You could be still chewing a piece of thick seam two weeks after you started eating it. It was like eating an obese rubber whelk. Tripe filled you up and stayed in the stomach for hours so one way of 'nobbling' a greyhound was to feed it a meal of raw tripe prior to the race. The poor, doped animal would start its race at ten minutes to one and cross the finishing line at a quarter to midnight.

People in the South of England would also consume tripe, but never raw. Instead, like our Gallic allies across the channel, they would stew it in milk with plenty of onions. Other speciality dishes were savoury ducks. They were faggots of dubious constituency, and neither looked, nor tasted, like ducks.

UCP cafés were seen as an attempt to cross social boundaries. The waitresses in these dining establishments wore a black and white corporate uniform. A black skirt and top was complemented with a white apron and bonnet. This sombre outfit was designed to match the black and white tiles displayed on the walls of the shop. The uniform also gave a touch of class and an impression that meals would be presented silver service. It was actually far from this presentation because Elsie received an occasional complaint about some Saturday girl junior waitress serving a plate of kidneys and mash, with their thumbprint in the gravy.

Some cafés had an upstairs restaurant that tended to be patronised by white-collar workers and professionals. Doctor Goldstein would pop in there for his weekly shot of liver, chips and gravy. The twenty-three stone Alderman Frank Jessop would increase his daily calorie count and feed on a double helping of steak and cow-heel pie, gravy and rissoles. He proclaimed that this nutritious boost gave him the energy to deal with the Highways Department in the afternoon. Elsie also catered for parties and the most unusual booking she took was for a wedding breakfast that cleaned her out of steamed steak puddings and other bovine tit bits. The only non-animal-based item on the menu that day was the wedding cake.

The tastiest component of any meal served at a UCP café was the gravy. Customers would salivate like Pavlov's dogs at the sight or smell of this substance. Its chemistry was known only to Elsie and Marion. Its fluidity was just right, not too viscous and not too runny. It would gently flow over pies and faggots and spread itself evenly over mash or chips. It was a taste to die for, unlike its culinary partners of brawn, elder and rissoles, whose lipid/cholesterol ingredients were tastes to die from. Workmen visiting the downstairs café would jest they were there for a two-course meal – chips and gravy. It was a Michelin experience to dunk your chips in the sumptuous gravy then suck it off the chip.

A typical weekday dinner-time saw the queue for a seat in the café stretching outside. The shop also provided a hot meal takeaway service as long as you brought your own pot or bowl to carry the order. Young kids were often dispatched to the UCP for the main meal of the day and would return home with a casserole dish full of UCP delights, and a tea towel over its top to keep them warm.

'And don't go nickin' any of them chips on the way home, our Anthony! If ya do, yer dad'll give yer a good pastin'!' Anthony couldn't resist the smell of the delicacies emanating from below the towel, and so down went five chips. 'I'll take the pastin', Anthony decided.

A favourite takeaway was steak and cow-heel pie. Elsie had a wonderful recipe for mass-producing this pastry-lined *bonne bouche*. She would use stewing beef mixed with fetlock cuts and mix in onion and small amounts of sage. The heel or fetlock produced an unctuous lip-sticking gravy that was retained within the pie until you punctured its pastry shell. Workmen would pop into the café for a steak and cow-heel pie, or as they frequently called them 'growler pies'. This nickname came from the noise these people made as they attacked the delectable suet crust to reveal the juicy insides. At one shilling and three pence it was a complete meal. Again, there was nothing more flavoursome than sucking this liquor as you chewed its meat content. These pies were truly appreciated if you held them in your hand to eat. Knives and forks were for those clearly living above their station.

Some factory girls would send out for pies or sandwiches. Madge Fraser would eat tongue sandwiches three times a week. Her supervisor would blame this consumption on her ability to gossip. Mary Carson from the same mill would regularly bring to work pig's cheek or haslet. She was the only woman known to be able to apply her lipstick while chewing a haslet sandwich. Ronnie Pickup, a carder at Cobden Street Mill, was renowned for purchasing and consuming a raw, horse-shoe-shaped black pudding from Elsie's café. He ate this daily, and his workmates accused him of looking over-wrought at the end of the week because of its high iron content. His wife jested that when he died she'd get twenty quid for him for scrap.

Elsie ran a good shop. She had a disciplined team who each knew their jobs. The two ladies who were responsible for the cold counter would dress that marble plinth so that even jellied pigs' trotters would look appealing. The centre-piece of the display was tripe laid out in overlaps. Around this mound were the chitterlings, pots of brawn, plates of elder. Elder was a form of pink-looking pate whose taste and smell went straight to your stomach. Black puddings and savoury ducks appeared in the next sector, giving the display both colour and appeal.

Around the edges would be sprigs of green plastic parsley and packets of beef dripping. This picture of carnivorous delights was reinforced by the aroma of cooked dishes such as steak and kidney done in a gelatinous roux or liver and onions, with the liver slices as light as an angel's kiss. The shop window, even in the summer time, was misted over. The steam from the kitchens did battle with the cold, damp air around the raw tripe. One of Elsie's junior girls would have to wipe the black and white tiled walls as well as the shop window.

Elsie was the head chef as well as carrying out managerial duties such as staffing and ordering. She did the books for the area UCP territorial manager. She was meticulous about every aspect of her duties. Her work started at 6.30 a.m. A quick brew of tea and Marion would arrive shortly after. Vegetables were chopped and pastry was made. Lambs' liver and kidneys were sliced all by eight o'clock. At this hour the cold produce shop ladies started work, along with a couple of waitresses to deal with breakfasts. Egg and bacon barm cakes, sausage, black pudding and scallops. Scallops were slices of potato cooked in a light batter and any surplus liquor was mopped up with two slices of bread. The breakfast menu was determined by the customer and there were endless combinations and possibilities. The float was put in the till, and the shop frontage dressed. The urn was on constantly through the day, its steam puffing away like a railway engine. Trading in the shop started at 8.30 a.m., whereas breakfasts were well under way by then. By mid-morning as many as two hundred people had been served and there was a much welcome lull before the dinner-time rush started the feeding frenzy once more. One café regular made the bold statement that the café sold good, wholesome food, that sticks to yer ribs.

A Saturday dinner-time regular was Mrs Mavis Brockett. Mavis was a pianist hired by the local Essoldo cinema to play tunes for the audience before each screening. She would arrive at the café around twelve thirty, after the Saturday morning kids' show. This morning session was known locally as the 'thrupenny crush'. She hated this warm-up session, and she had threatened to leave on many occasions. 'It's them ruddy kids, I'm black and blue by the end of the film!' she would tell Elsie. Indeed, she would arrive at the café with bright red ears that had been peppered by pea shooters delivering hard, dried peas with a velocity of over forty miles per hour. On this particular morning, the coat that she wore, with its upturned collar designed to give her head some protection, was soaked. This was due to the kids running out of peas and so deciding to bombard her with a volley of water bombs.

'Give us a cup of tea, Elsie, and steak puddin' and gravy. I need something to calm me nerves! I ask ya, am I an artiste or an Aunt Sally at t' fairground? I've got standards ya know, Elsie. I was classically trained.'

It was during these times that a chain of coffee shops opened called the Kardomah Coffee Shops. There was one in neighbouring Manchester. It was an entirely different set up and organisation. There you could purchase tea and pastries but also consume the new-age drink of coffee. Visiting these premises and downing an apple Danish and a coffee made you feel middle class. It was now up to Elsie's UCP café to compete with this bistro. The closest she'd got in the past to the Kardomah menu was to offer Horlicks and hot Bovril. It was now time to offer the exotic libation of coffee. The nearest she had ever come to this beverage before was Camp coffee with its distinctive chicory essence. Elsie's gran had won a bottle of this in the church tombola. She attempted to drink this wonder preparation and spat it into the fire, ranting 'That stuff is 'orrible! Are ya tryin' to ruddy poison me, our Elsie? Awful stuff. It'll never catch on.'

Shortly after Elsie's attempt at senecide, coffee appeared on her café menu. The Jessie Maidment troupe of tea guzzlers sat at their usual table at the usual time. 'Is it four teas, girls?' enquired Elsie.

'Yes please, and mind there aren't any chips on the cups like there were last time, Mrs Turnbull,' Jessie replied without looking at her as she took her seat.

'Well, you can always sup elsewhere, Mrs Maidment!' shouted Elsie.

'We're fine here, if you please,' Mrs Maidment retorted.

'How about trying one of our coffees? They're all the rage nowadays. Go on ladies, be adventurous. I tell you what, why don't you try one Mrs Maidment, being a lady of knowledge, class and breeding? If you don't like it, I won't charge you for it. Can't be fairer than that,' offered Elsie.

'I know all there is to know about coffee, thank you very much,' Jessie paused … 'Free you say? Go on then I'll have one. It better be good, I was drinking coffee before you were born.'

'Right then, Mrs Maidment. Do you want it black or white?' asked Elsie.

'Err,' hesitated Jessie, 'black? Yes, I'll have black,' she replied with an air of confidence and wisdom. 'Oh and put plenty o' milk in it an' all.'

# Mrs Anderton
# at Number 8

DOREEN ANDERTON WAS AN usherette at the Central Cinema, two
streets away from Copenhagen Street. It was one of the oldest
cinemas in the city and because its location was in the poorest enclave
of the area, its clientele were often perceived as being a hard audience
to please. There was never a queue outside. People just drifted in,
perhaps halfway through a film and would watch its end. Then they
would view the beginning of the story, and make sense of these two
segments. This was not a good move, particularly if the film was a
whodunnit. Mind you, it was sometimes just good to get out of the
rain.

There were three usherettes at the Central, and in an effort to raise
the profile of this establishment, the manager Kurt D'Angelo, whose
real name was Norris Broadbent, bought this female trio bright yellow
outfits, each with a red plastic belt. There was a slight drawback to
such corporate attire in that when they were selling ice creams at the
interval, the light from the battery powered bulb in the ice cream tray
reflected upwards and bounced off their bright yellow coats. It made
them look jaundiced. In fact Doreen grew to ignore requests like 'Two
tubs, love, and I hope your malaria gets better.'

In one of their pockets was a black rubber-coated torch tipped with
a red border. The torch was constructed so that it emitted parallel

beams of light designed to highlight painted seat and row numbers for patrons. Indeed, the inside of this cinema was extremely dark. The lights in the auditorium were never switched on even between the films so as not to reveal the mould growing on the walls of the building. Patrons entering the auditorium from outside would immediately suffer night blindness. It was like walking into the abyss. Unfortunately, there was a step that led into the body of the theatre and even with the help of the usherette's torch, the sound of people crashing to the floor was regularly heard. Several eager patrons stepped off this ledge and crashed head-first into a fire extinguisher. This object immediately responded to the collision of cranium against metal with the sound of a church bell. Such trauma was accompanied by the familiar expletives of 'Oh shite!' or 'Bloody hell fire!' as they checked themselves for broken bones. Their painful cries were matched by unsympathetic outbursts from a seventy-five-year-old lady who shouted 'Do ya mind? I'm tryin' to watch t'ruddy film!'

Doreen was a middle-aged lady who lived at the bottom of Copenhagen Street with her 'fancy man' as people called him. Lester Gomersall was far from being fancy. He was bone-idle. Her sister would often say, 'I don't know what our Doreen sees in him, I really don't. Idle Jack they should call him. She has to get him out of bed every morning by waving her torch in his eyes. She even feeds him a choc ice for breakfast an' all. Takes her job seriously does our Doreen.'

Doreen's other two colleagues at the cinema were young twin sisters, Beryl and Nadine Golightly. Both were work shy and had to be frequently reprimanded by Kurt. They would be found filing their nails or gossiping in the foyer. They both had peroxide blonde hair and constantly chewed gum. These nymphets always wore a chiffon scarf to mask the love bites around their necks. Nadine once turned up for work looking as though she had been savaged by Sumo leaches. Doreen and the twins never got on. She claimed that in the two years they had worked at the Central, their torch batteries were as fresh as the day they had been purchased. Beryl was particularly flirtatious and would wolf whistle at every passing teddy-boy. These lads, with their creamed DAs and bunch-of-grapes hairstyles, would make squeaky noises with their crepe-soled shoes on the linoleum floor of the cinema's foyer. One poor lad, with his drainpipe trousers, had been a victim of rickets in his early years, and from behind it looked as though his torso had been mounted on a Hoola-Hoop.

The audience sat on wooden seats, rather than the comfortable, upholstered ones found in the more up market cinemas in Manchester. You often had to use a pair of tweezers to remove splinters, having been seated on some of the chairs. Women would refuse to wear nylons because of the ladders inflicted by these roughened seats. Cries of, 'These were brand new on tonight these! Just look at 'em now. I look as though I've been mauled by a ruddy tiger!' This was obviously not the case, however; she had just been groped by an over amorous boyfriend on the back row.

The ambiance of this place was not helped by the waft of lower bowel movements and urine that drifted on occasions from the medieval toilets. This unmistakable aroma would wind its way through the rows of seats. At the end of each week's listings the cleaner would attempt to neutralise this stench with bleach. The next house would leave its customers gasping for air in the chlorine-soaked atmosphere. Cleaner Eleanor Hargreaves would blame the atmosphere on blow back from the sewers and declare, 'They don't have to come 'ere if they don't want. You could eat yer dinner off one o' my piss stones after I've cleaned it, ya could.'

The cinema had unfortunately been positioned adjacent to a railway line. This took passengers from Manchester to such exotic places as Southport and Barrow-in-Furness. Trains would thunder along the railway cutting at all times of the day. Their roar would frequently obliterate the sound of the actors' voices, which was particularly annoying if it was a crucial moment in the plot. People would then ask each other, 'What did she say? Is he going to leave her or not?' Another disadvantage of the close proximity of the railway was that the patrons would vibrate in tandem with the projectionist. He tried desperately to hold down the projector during these passing excursions. His efforts at preventing this machine from moving across the room were often in vain. The likes of Victor Mature and Ingrid Bergman would perform like clockwork figures pulsating across the screen. However, the 1959 film 'The Last Days of Pompeii' was brought to life by the 8.35 from Heysham. It was hands-on stuff and the precursor of iMax cinema technology.

During the 1950s, and before the Clean Air Act, the city, like all industrial areas, was subject to smog in the winter months. This pernicious amalgam of oxides of nitrogen, carbon particles and sulphurous compounds did nothing for your respiratory tract. On very bad days when people walked along streets with a handkerchief or scarf over their mouths, the noxious wreaths of this cold air were seen to permeate the cinema audience. Its dense plasma could be observed creeping under the fire doors. Its dark yellow body would slowly shift as a penetrating miasma from pavement to foyer to auditorium. The curious fact was that people would continue to draw on their Capstan Full Strength and Park Drive cigarettes throughout this toxic assault.

In the more salubrious cinemas, everyone would stand for the national anthem at the end of a film. This was not the case at the Central. At the sight of the first credits on the screen people would flick up the wooden seats and noisily leave the cinema through the nearest exit, which was frequently the fire doors. There were few monarchists who attended the Central Cinema.

This picture house would specialise in cowboy films, so much so that its patrons would refer to the building as 'The Ranch'. Doreen would look forward to a Tex Ritter or a Gene Autry film.

'I love to watch 'em gallop across those endless Nevada plains. It's the only fresh air I get.'

Doreen had worked at the cinema for over ten years and was near word perfect on some of the classics of the forties. She would quote Trevor Howard, as Alec, in the greatest romantic film of all times, 'Brief Encounter'.

'Oh my dear, I love you so very much. I love you with all my heart and soul.'

Such romantic lines were lost on Lester Gomersall, who would break wind and then turn over, taking the complete eiderdown with him.

Doreen had watched Paul Heinreid make cigarette smoking a sensual act in the wonderful film 'Now Voyager', when he lit two cigarettes, one for his lover, Bette Davis. When she asked Lester to try this, his woodbine got stuck on his lip and he burned himself as he tried to pass her the cigarette.

The part of the week she did not enjoy, however, was the Saturday morning pictures for the local kids. They would call it the 'thrupenny crush'. She would call it a morning of hell. Kurt made her watch that everyone paid before entering the auditorium. This seemed a simple request but Doreen was dealing with some kids who, in years to come, would spend a portion of their lives in Strangeways prison. These kids would barge into the foyer and then one lad would create a commotion. Doreen would then have to sort out the matter, only for six of his mates to slip through and hide in the toilets until the film started. Worse was to follow. The young congregation was armed better than the parachute regiment. Water bombs were thrown huge distances onto some poor unsuspecting kids near the front. Pea shooters would fire dried peas with such velocity that they would hurt the lobes of your ears as they quickly came to rest. Pea guns, spud guns, catapults, lighted cigarette ends and itching powder would complete their arsenal.

During the interval, Doreen would be required to sell ice creams from her tray. She would slip on the halter and brave the aisle near the screen. She was instantly descended on by the paediatric population hungry for choc ices and tubs. There was little crowd control, and pushing and shoving was met with cries of 'Get back and stop shovin' yer little buggers!' or 'I said that's two shillin', not sixpence for those tubs. You've either got the money or not. And no I don't do a hire purchase, ya cheeky devil!'

Doreen was glad when the films started. There was less trouble then. Yes, you did get the smokers who would furtively pass a woodbine along a row, each recipient taking a good lung full. You did get the loud shaft of flatulence during a quiet scene. You did get the rustling of crisp and sweet bags. You did get the occasional cry of pain from some kid who wanted to go to the toilet and was tripped up along his journey. Doreen once had to deal with a young lad hit on the back of the head by a frozen Jubbly lobbed from five rows behind.

One of the most disruptive acts perpetrated by this motley crew was for someone to bring into the cinema a couple of matchboxes containing moths. These kids would sit on the back row in front of the projectionist's window. When the film started the prankster would open the matchboxes and release the four moths. These insects would instantly make for the light source and cause huge bat like shadows on the screen much to the amusement of the rest of the kids. Doreen was immediately dispatched by Kurt to catch these creatures. After many

attempts at swatting them, Kurt arrived complete with a large Flit Fly Spray and gassed them, smothering the back two rows of patrons with this noxious stuff at the same time.

Kurt also dreaded the projectionist breaking the film. Suddenly the screen would blanche and then turn eerily black. This was the signal for the audience to stamp on the floor and shout incessantly, 'Why are we waiting?' The din continued until either Kurt was forced on stage or the man behind the projector managed to tape the broken, burnt celluloid together. Kurt would rant at the youngsters and shake his fist. You could tell he meant business when the veins on his neck started to protrude. His face would glow with anger and his admonishment usually ended with some urchin being banned from the cinema. Doreen felt powerless in dealing with such recidivists. It was usually the case that Doreen would shine her torch on some miscreant and shout, 'Hey, you in the red balaclava! Do that again and yer out!' The little chap in the red headgear did it again and Kurt would then wade through a sea of knees, grab the youth by his pullover, and then proceed to throw him out of the cinema onto the street.

The cinema projectionist was a middle-aged man named Oscar Tomlinson. Oscar lived in a room above a sweet and tobacco shop in Clement Street. He had suffered badly from alopecia in his youth and decided to mask this disability by wearing a National Health issue toupée. I am uncertain as to the cause of the problem but Oscar's hairpiece never seemed to fit. Whether it was the contours of his scalp or its lack of adhesion, I know not. Were he to turn his head quickly, the wig would stay still, leaving Oscar with a parting at right angles to his face. When Oscar was under stress, such as when the celluloid film melted or the film snapped, during the minutes when he remedied the problem he would sweat profusely. The hairy prosthesis would then float forward on a sea of perspiration and cover half of his face. Kids looking through the projector window at the back of the room would be terrified to see this half man, half yeti creature, surrounded by yards of 35 mm film.

Another challenge concerning maintaining order was the inevitable stampede to vacate the cinema at the end of the morning session. Following the roar of disappointment when the message 'TO BE CONTINUED NEXT WEEK' was flashed up on the screen, hundreds of kids would crash through the fire exit doors and let much-needed light and air into the building. Kids just didn't want to wait another week to see if the goody's girlfriend was going to be squashed by a steam engine. They wanted to know right now if the baddy would get his comeuppance from the goody for having tied his lover onto the railway track. As part of their protest they would leave behind a sea of debris along the rows of seats. It was the cleaner's job to then tidy the picture house ready for the evening programme. It was amazing what she would discover. Amongst the crisp and sweet packets, empty ice cream tubs and their wooden spoons, would be a pair of soiled underpants or an unexploded water bomb filled with wee. Someone once let off an air bomb firework that nearly set the place on fire. All in all, it was a tough morning for Doreen and Kurt.

The matinee and evening performances also kept Doreen on her toes. She would receive complaints from some old lady and gentleman sitting immediately in front of the back row where it was customary for courting couples to do their canoodling. On occasions this amorous behaviour went a little too far, forcing the old lady to turn around and poke the budding Romeo with her umbrella and shout, 'Good God lad, you sound as though you've had no dinner. Leave her face alone!'

Kurt had warned his usherettes as to the possible dangers of unaccompanied men in the audience and what they may get up to. Doreen was once called to a pair of hysterical girls who had been spoken to by a middle-aged man in a gabardine mackintosh sitting next to them. They both screamed at Doreen and shouted, 'This bloke has just said to us, if you want it, it's underneath my hat!' The gentleman, as both Doreen and Kurt both discovered, was not talking about a packet of Dolly Mixtures.

There was a rumour that Kurt fancied Doreen. Indeed, someone once said he held a torch for her. This was particularly true when Doreen tumbled down the infamous step leading into the rear stalls and broke her arm. Kurt was seen, complete with Doreen's torch, showing the punters to their seats.

Doreen continued working at the Central Cinema until it closed in 1959. It was also in that year that Lester proposed, not to her but to Marcia Posset, a notorious lady of the evening who plied her trade near the docks. On winter nights, she preferred to work nearer to home at the Craven Heifer pub. Doreen discovered the two of them in flagrante delicto, as it were, in an alleyway between the cinema and

Copenhagen Street. She heard some groaning noise coming from inside the dark ginnel and shone her works issue torch to see what was happening. Lester claimed the lady had fainted and he was putting her in the recovery position and he was seeing if she was breathing, to which Doreen replied, 'The recovery position? Checkin' if she were breathin'? So why were yer trousers round yer ankles then?'

Immediately following Lester's unorthodox attempt at First Aid, he was thrown out of Number 30, a move that saved Doreen numerous torch batteries and choc ices too.

# Saint Sebastian's Church

IT WAS ONE HELL of a knock. A real rent man's knock. The thump was so hard it foretold both purpose and determination. My dad said it would have woken the dead. The assailant of our front door was, in fact, Father Dolan, and not our rent man.

Father Podraig Dolan was one of three priests attached to Saint Sebastian's church, whose tall spire dominated the landscape on the main road, opposite our street. He had been diocesan priest at the church for over twenty years. The bishop had clearly overlooked this man of God, and had failed to move him on. The practice of transferring priests seemed common in most parishes. Father Dolan had been left to maintain the fear of God in his parishioners and uphold traditional values. The trouble was, these standards were both outdated and draconian. Such a philosophy did nothing to endear him to the working class community, who struggled to get by after the Second World War.

I can only describe the gentleman as a pious fossil whose antiquated ideology and lack of interpersonal skills gave him the nickname 'Rasputin'. Pastoral care to him was for his flock to say the Hail Mary, The Glory Be, and an Our Father three times plus a reminder that God knows and sees everything. Poor fourteen-year-old Philip Desmond was always a mystery to Father Dolan. Philip wore shiny black, patent leather sandals, and he would insist on wearing his mum's green, paisley nylon scarf. His occasional use of lipstick and rose water made Saturday afternoon confession an uncomfortable procedure for Father Dolan. Unbelievably long penances were issued to the young lad. Such punishment was usually supported by instructions to 'Pull yourself together, boy!' and 'Away with this nonsense!' Orders of this nature didn't seem to help Philip come to terms with his sexual identity. It also was at odds with Father Dolan's frequent message from the pulpit that 'God loves everyone'.

Funerals, christenings and marriages were services he performed with the same remoteness and indifference. Mrs Dora Leeky had been a committed Roman Catholic since she was a foetus, and visited him for spiritual counsel when she discovered her husband in bed with her sister. His languid prescription for this injured soul was that Mr Leeky, a self-confessed heretic, would burn in hell and be damned forever. Such a powerful proclamation didn't seem to bother Mr Leeky who then continued to live 'over the brush' with his wife's sister until he reached the age of ninety-two, and showed no sign of fire damage.

My dad answered what was left of the front door and seemed surprised to see the priest. The holy man didn't bother to be asked into our house, he just walked straight into the living room.

'Oh, do come in Father,' my dad sarcastically commented as the man now approached the kitchen table. He made straight for my mum who was also an Irish Catholic. Father Dolan never talked to my dad because he refused to attend mass. Instead he always chose to ignore him, and rather like Mr Leeky, my dad was deemed to be future candidate for incineration at the devil's pleasure.

'Mrs Bracegirdle,' he said. His introduction to my mum was punctuated with gasps for air. Father Dolan would never be awarded medals for compassion but he would certainly have been recognised for his services to the tobacco industry. He was a chain smoker and would often pop out of the confessional box for a few puffs of Capstan Full Strength. Rumour was that he would fill the silver incense jar with a mixture biased towards Old Holborn rather than frankincense.

'I have just received the news that your son Gerard has passed his Eleven Plus,' he continued, as his mouth clutched passing pockets of air.

'Ooooh, yes Father, and we're ever so pleased,' replied my mother, giving him chance to load his lungs once more.

'The thing is, Mrs Bracegirdle, I hear he's not going to the Catholic boys' grammar school. This is not good news, Mrs Bracegirdle. It's not good news at all!' His last sentence was followed by a prolonged bout of coughing, and his cheeks became redder following each hack. His round, fat, varicose face now looked as though he'd been sitting by a furnace for half an hour.

I had, indeed, passed my Eleven Plus. I was a member of the post-war baby-boomers, and our large population meant that some of us left footers were too great in number to be absorbed into the local Catholic grammar school. Instead, our excess meant we were to attend the Protestant grammar school. This downgrade, as Father Dolan would call it, seemed fine by me, and my dad. However, the great man himself was the prophet of doom, and here he was to persuade my mum that this pagan seat of learning would corrupt my spiritual future. His thoughts were that I'd eventually join my dad and Mr Leeky for a roasting in Hades.

After much heated discussion, it was decided to reach a compromise. The end product of this fiery debate, fuelled by Father Dolan's intransigence, was that I should attend Saint Sebastian's presbytery every Saturday morning for 'instruction'. I was unclear about the meaning of this word. Was it to warn me of Protestant ways like supporting Manchester City instead of United? Could it be for me to make the sign of the cross and say 'Forgive them Father, for they know not what they do', in every RE lesson? Whatever it was going to be, it certainly didn't sound like it was going to break down sectarian barriers but to strengthen them.

I recall my first trip to the presbytery on a Saturday morning. I knocked on its oak door several times. Nobody in, I thought, and was just about to return home when the door did open and there stood Mrs Wetherall, the priest's housekeeper. The lady was dressed in black and her hair was drawn back across her scalp, and finished in a tight bun at the back of her head. The hairstyle made her look fierce, and what compounded such facial misery was that she never smiled. I suppose looking after three lugubrious agents of God for many years had crafted her sullen persona.

I didn't know what was in store for us on that morning. Behind Mrs Wetherall was a large statue of some bearded bloke nailed to a cross. There was blood all over him! As an innocent eleven-year-old it made me wonder if he'd also gone to a Protestant school and had refused Saturday morning instruction from Father Dolan. Mrs Wetherall observed the unease my face reflected and she sharply asked me what was the matter.

'Oh, errr … nothing, I'm here for instruction,' I said.

'Take your cap off and go in that room over there. And wipe your feet! Have you no manners?' she shouted as she prodded me in the direction of a dark doorway.

I would soon find out that Saturday morning sessions with Father Dolan meant learning, word for word, the catechism. For those unfamiliar with this term, the catechism is a summary of the principles of Christian religion in the form of questions and answers – not just a few, but hundreds of them! To me, and the majority of the other Catholic Eleven Plus casualties who also had to attend instruction, such pointless learning of statements such as 'God made me to know him, love him and serve him in this world and forever in the next,' all proved too much. By the time we had completed the first term at the heathen, Protestant grammar school, we noticed we weren't burning in hell each lesson. Mutiny was afoot and we all packed in Father Dolan's instruction. Eddie Barber, a short, skinny lad from Irvine Street, was the main instigator of the rebellion.

'I ain't learnin' this cataclysm, no more!' he shouted, as he jumped up from his chair in the presbytery. Eddie had just received the weekly total of no marks out of ten for the regular Saturday morning test and was currently being scolded by Father Dolan.

'And another thing ya won't like,' shouted Eddie, 'when I say the Lord's Prayer, I always say our Father who farts in heaven!' This last sentence was delivered as he slammed the presbytery door behind him. I thought the holy man was about to explode, for his customary red face now turned crimson. The veins in his neck and face stood out like flashing neon signs. Well, Father, you win some, you lose some, and it looked like you just lost Eddie.

Father Dolan upheld the sacrament of marriage. He gave prenuptial instruction to couples about to embark on a lifetime of happiness. My father had agreed to accept this guidance so that my mother could be married in church. Dad was an agnostic and found all of this preparation rather intense. In an effort to make light of things during one particularly rigorous session, he asked for one of the hymns at the wedding to be 'Fight the good fight'. The holy man didn't see the funny side of things and warned my mother she was making a big mistake marrying my dad.

Around the time of the religious instruction debacle, Father Pascoe, a priest also attached to St Sebastian's, and older than Father Dolan, died. A young priest, Father Wood, straight out of training school, was installed as a replacement. He did look young. Mind you, anything would look young compared to the prehistoric Father Dolan.

It soon became obvious to the parishioners that Father Wood brought a much-needed breath of fresh air to the church. People would queue up outside his confessional. Nobody wanted Dolan to hear your sins for you would be certain to receive a verbal lashing on top of a sea of repentance prayers. I would never tell him all of my sins because I knew I'd be paying for them for hours doing my penance. I once overheard Uncle Tommy, my mum's brother, telling dad that he wasn't going to confess about 'fiddling' his ration book in case Father Dolan sent him to Siberia. I too would keep quiet about my adolescent fantasies about naked women. I imagined all sorts of penances, from emasculation to imprisonment for those thoughts!

Father Wood's popularity was also reflected by the wishes of young couples to be married by him and to have him christen their children. Matrimony conducted by Father Dolan was a procedure undertaken without much emotion. He always encouraged a nuptial mass where both bride and groom took communion. This was always hard on your knees because of the length of the service. However, should the bride be pregnant at the altar then the ageing father would refuse such a service, having previously informed them of his displeasure at their carnal antics. It was custom for Catholic families to invite the priest to the wedding breakfast and Father Dolan was always seated next to the granny of the family, whose deafness made him easy to tolerate.

Christenings were over and done with as quickly as possible. The babies always cried as the holy man emptied water down their throat. Everyone around the font got a good soaking. The order of the day was wear your best clothes underneath a sou' wester. Dolan's dexterity with babies left mum and dad really believing he was going to drop their new-born.

In sharp contrast, Father Wood's manner with people showed a warmth, care and concern. He actually seemed pleased when married couples asked him to baptise their progeny. They welcomed his sermons that focused on contemporary issues. After all, they had been used to years of repent ye sinners and fear God's wrath. Eleven o'clock mass was seen as a family gathering and numbers more than doubled when Father Wood conducted the service.

Father Wood understood that keeping youth on the side of the church meant the church had a future. To facilitate this he helped run the new cycling proficiency scheme. However, he soon found that in the very poor parts of the parish, where the pawnbroker was visited more than the grocer, bicycles were hard to come by. The better-off parts of the city suddenly noticed a rash of bicycle thefts during these times, and the majority of these bikes finished up in houses along Roscoe Street and in Hardacre Terrace, adjacent to Saint Sebastian's church. The rent man for these impoverished residences was extremely familiar with the principle of 'moonlight flits', when mounting rent arrears forced the family's sudden overnight disappearance.

Another way of keeping the youth alongside the church was for Father Wood to organise a church under-fifteen football team for the boys and to persuade Sister Mary Louise from the nearby convent to run a similar netball squad for the girls. Both ventures were inexpensive, the church having only to purchase the balls. Kit was out of the question. Any opposition they played would run on the shirts-out/shirts-in principle. Such economics proved cost effective except for tiny twelve-year-old Dominic Mulvaney of Lissadel Street. He always wore a bright red chunky polo neck sweater that finished above his navel, the whole year through. He didn't possess a shirt to his name. After trying to make him wear one of his dad's work shirts, Father Wood gave up as he said he looked like Wee Willy Winkie playing on the left wing. Eventually, after much negotiation with his dad, Father Wood selected him as goalkeeper so that he could continue to wear his red sweater that his gran had knitted for him.

The whole team was rejigged because of the 'Dominic shirt controversy'. Such positional changes proved beneficial for the team because Derek Swinburn's rickets made him an appalling goalkeeper. He would leak goals, right, left and most certainly centre. At least Dominic's legs remained constantly parallel.

Success came quickly for the team. We demolished St Xavier's, five-nil. Two of our goals were scored by Eddie Barber who had now become a born again Christian. Eddie guaranteed Father Wood that he would attend Sunday mass and also stop himself saying 'Our Father who farts in heaven', if he could play inside right.

Before long, our team finished in the finals of the under-fifteen Catholic boys' football final played at 'The Cliff', Manchester United's training ground. The Bishop of Salford was a great friend of Sir Matt Busby and this Catholic bond secured the venue. Father Wood was manager, coach, club doctor and linesman. He seemed to do everything with passion and good will. He even hammered new studs into the only four pairs of football boots that our squad possessed. They were leather studs, bashed in with nails. Our team must have looked a sorry sight. Tommy Fraser turned up complete with nit lotion on his hair, James Warburton insisted playing in his shoes, basically because it was the only footwear he possessed. Even worse was Paul Foggerty in his wellies. Laurence Thomas's mother insisted Laurence should keep on his mustard plaster because of his weak chest. Mind you, Laurence's plaster came in very handy when your mother had cut you a boiled ham sandwich, you could rub it on the plaster and the flavour was magnificent.

The day of the final arrived and we all travelled down to the ground together. A real surprise for us was that fathers Dolan and Everett accompanied our team. I suppose the game was a place for the local priests to meet up and discuss boring things like attendances, church repairs and fund raising. Another venture that Father Wood pioneered was the weekly raffle and tombola. My gran won a bottle of Camp coffee in the latter and vowed never to participate again as she said coffee was disgusting stuff and nearly poisoned her.

We were amazed at the pitch. It was covered in grass! Our normal playing surface was either cobbled streets, cinder crofts or bald football pitches covered with compacted clay. If your boots had studs, then running on this surface sounded like a cattle stampede.

It was a capacity crowd as Father Wood pointed out, though I was certain the word capacity didn't mean twenty-five. Our team was at near full-strength, with Tosh Walker at centre half. Tosh was tall for his age and when you were stood next to him you could see right up his nose. Barney Cohen was our centre forward. Barney was Jewish, and I could never work out what he was doing in our team. Maybe the rabbi at his synagogue had given him a free transfer?

The game kicked off and we were two-nil up at half time with both goals coming from Barney's left foot. Father Wood was giving the team-talk in the dressing room when suddenly the door was thrown open, and there stood Father Dolan, his face beaming with delight.

'Lads!' he shouted as he entered the room, carefully slipping his hip flask into his overcoat pocket. He held his arms high.

'It's great to see you play. Good, Catholic lads. And do you see what you can do with the Lord on your side? And all of yas from good Catholic families, too!' I did notice everyone look at Barney at that point in his eulogy.

'Take this young feller,' he pointed to young Liam Dougan. 'Playin' his heart out, so he is. A good, Catholic lad he is, from a devoted Catholic family. Tell me, Liam, is your older brother not playin' today?'

'Errr, no Father. He's gone with me mam to visit me dad,' replied little Liam.

'Sure, I didn't know he was in hospital. I'll say a couple of rosaries for him, so I will. In hospital, you say?'

'No Father. He's in Walton jail for nickin' lead from St Xavier's roof,' replied the good Catholic boy from the good Catholic family.

Again Father, you win some, you lose some.